10 minute
Maths
Assessments

for ages 7-8

CONTENTS

Assessment for learning

It is widely acknowledged that effective learning takes place where teachers understand their pupils' standards of achievement and lead the pupils forwards from these standards.

> *Assessment for learning is the process of seeking and interpreting evidence for use by learners and their teachers to decide where the learners are in their learning, where they need to go and how best to get there.*
>
> *(Assessment for Learning: 10 principles – Assessment Reform Group)*

This book will help you to assess your pupils' progress by providing activities that are quick and easy to administer, that can be used on a regular basis and that will help you build a profile of each pupil's attainment. Each activity will provide you with evidence of achievement that you can use for on-going pupil assessment and will help you focus your teaching and planning on the specific learning requirements of each child in your class.

Using the materials in this book will provide opportunities for both formative and summative assessment. It is recommended that the activities are used on a regular basis as part of an ordinary maths lesson, for continuous formative assessment. Recording the progress of each pupil, using the recording grid provided, will also assist you in making regular summative assessments in relation to National Curriculum levels of attainment.

All aspects of the *Framework for mathematics* for Year 3 are addressed through the assessment of separate learning objectives. These learning objectives are drawn from Strands 2 to 7 of the Framework:

2. Counting and understanding number
3. Knowing and using number facts
4. Calculating
5. Understanding shape
6. Measuring
7. Handling data

Many of the activities can also be used to support your assessment of Strand 1 (*Using and applying mathematics*). The teachers' notes accompanying each activity indicate where an assessment is particularly relevant to this.

How to use the activities for assessing pupils' progress

Ideally, pupils will work with an adult on an individual basis or in a very small group to enable the adult to make effective judgements about each individual's achievement. Everything achieved by the pupil should be a learning experience, perhaps where a particular skill or an aspect of knowledge is being strengthened and consolidated, or where a style of layout or method is being encountered for the first time. However, the assessment activities should only be used when the pupil has some prior experience of the work being assessed.

A pupil may be able to complete some, but not all, of the learning objectives. Any adult working closely with a pupil may discover 'gaps' in their understanding that can be reported back to the class teacher for monitoring and planning purposes. Further practice, focusing on specific areas, will help to fill these gaps and the assessment can then be repeated when the pupil is ready.

What's on the CD

The CD that accompanies this book can be used on a computer or CD player and features an audio track that can be used for the assessments that require audio. Children are often more focused when listening to a recording as the sound of a different voice helps to hold their attention. The teachers' notes for each assessment indicate whether there is an accompanying audio track and its number on the CD.

The CD also includes a recording grid on which you can indicate whether individual children have achieved specific learning objectives. You may decide not to use all the assessments with every pupil. In some cases, you might feel that you already have sufficient evidence that a child has achieved the specific objective and so leave it out. You may also decide to complete the assessments in a different order from the order in this book.

By filling in the the recording grid you will be able to build a clear picture of an individual's strengths and weaknesses as well as the class as a whole. The recording grid can be used to form an evidence base for assessing the National Curriculum level of each pupil, i.e. summative assessment. Your school or local authority will provide guidance regarding interpretation of evidence to make decisions about pupils' levels. Each pupil will be deemed to have reached a 'low', 'secure' or 'high' standard against the level criteria. Our recording grid uses these 'standards' (with red for 'low', orange for 'secure' and green for 'high') in relation to each 'I can' statement to help you make appropriate decisions about the progress of each pupil and how you might focus your teaching on each pupil's learning requirements.

Note that assessments are **not** provided for the following statements from the *Framework for mathematics* as these can be adequately covered in day-to-day experiences:

- Relate 3-D solids to drawings of them

- Describe, visualise, classify and make 3-D solids

- Know the relationships between kilometres and metres, metres and centimetres, kilograms and grams, litres and millilitres; choose and use appropriate units to estimate, measure and record measurements

- Read, to the nearest division and half-division, scales that are numbered or partially numbered; use the information to measure and draw to a suitable degree of accuracy

- Calculate time intervals and find start or end times for a given time interval

Read, write and order whole numbers to at least 1000

Building on previous learning

Before starting this unit check that the children can already:

- read and write two-digit and three-digit numbers in figures and words.

Learning objectives

Objective 1: Read numbers to at least 1000.
Objective 2: Write numbers to at least 1000.
Objective 3: Order numbers to at least 1000.

Learning outcomes

The children will be able to:

- read two-digit, three-digit and four-digit numbers in figures.
- write two-digit, three-digit and four-digit numbers in figures.
- write two-digit, three-digit and four-digit numbers in order.

Success criteria

The children have a **secure** level of attainment in relation to Objective 1 if the following questions can be answered with a 'yes'.

Can the children...
... read aloud the numbers shown in figures on the Assessment sheet?
... match the numbers in figures to the numbers in words?

The children have a **secure** level of attainment in relation to Objective 2 if the following question can be answered with a 'yes'.

Can the children...
... write the numbers in figures that are dictated on the CD?

The children have a **secure** level of attainment in relation to Objective 3 if the following question can be answered with a 'yes'.

Can the children...
... write the numbers that are dictated on the CD in order?

Administering the assessment

⏺ Track 1 Ideally the children should work in a small group with an adult. For the first part of the assessment ask the children to read the numbers in figures as you point to them randomly. You could extend the activity by asking them to join the numbers in figures to the matching numbers in words. The CD can be used for the second part of the activity, though you might decide to read the instructions (shown below) to the children instead.

Find box a. Write the number 362 in the box.
Write the number 1218 in box b.
Write the number 1000 in box c.
Write the number 802 in box d.
Write the number 450 in box e.
Write the number 78 in box f.
Look at box g.
The numbers in box g are 419, 914, 491, 1149 and 941. Write the numbers in order, from smallest to largest.
Look at box h.
The numbers in box h are 270, 1027, 720, 702 and 207. Write the numbers in order, from smallest to largest.

(This assessment will also provide evidence for assessing strand 1, Using and applying mathematics: Identify patterns and relationships involving numbers.)

Andrew Brodie: Ten Minute Maths Assessments ages 7–8 © A&C Black 2009

Read, write and order whole numbers to at least 1000

Name

Date

Can you read the numbers in figures and in words?

210	four hundred and seventeen
999	eight hundred and forty-two
417	two hundred and ten
375	one thousand, two hundred and forty-three
842	nine hundred and ninety-nine
627	six hundred and twenty-seven
1243	three hundred and seventy-five

Listen carefully to the CD or your teacher.

a ⬚ b ⬚ c ⬚ d ⬚ e ⬚ f ⬚

g

| 419 | 914 | 491 | 1149 | 941 |

h

| 270 | 1027 | 720 | 702 | 207 |

I can read three-digit and four-digit numbers in figures. ⬚

I can write three-digit and four-digit numbers in figures. ⬚

I can write three-digit and four-digit numbers in order. ⬚

Andrew Brodie: Ten Minute Maths Assessments ages 7–8 © A&C Black 2009

Position numbers to at least 1000 on a number line

Building on previous learning

Before starting this unit check that the children can already:
- read and write two-digit and three-digit numbers in figures and words.

Learning objectives

Objective 1: Order numbers to at least 1000 and position them on a number line.

Learning outcomes

The children will be able to:
- estimate positions of three-digit and four-digit numbers in relation to a number line.

Success criteria

The children have a **secure** level of attainment in relation to Objective 1 if the following question can be answered with a 'yes'.

Can the children…
… position the numbers provided in appropriate places on the number lines?

Administering the assessment

Ideally the children should work in a small group with an adult. Encourage each child to read each number and then to look closely at the number line and to explain the appropriate position for that number. This discussion will enable you to assess each child's understanding of relative values of numbers – the writing of the number in the correct place provides further evidence. The children will need to be aware that the number lines are not all the same.

(This assessment will also provide evidence for assessing strand 1, Using and applying mathematics: Identify patterns and relationships involving numbers.)

Andrew Brodie: Ten Minute Maths Assessments ages 7–8 © A&C Black 2009

Position numbers to at least 1000 on a number line

Name

Date

Look carefully at each number.
Write the number in the correct place on the number line.

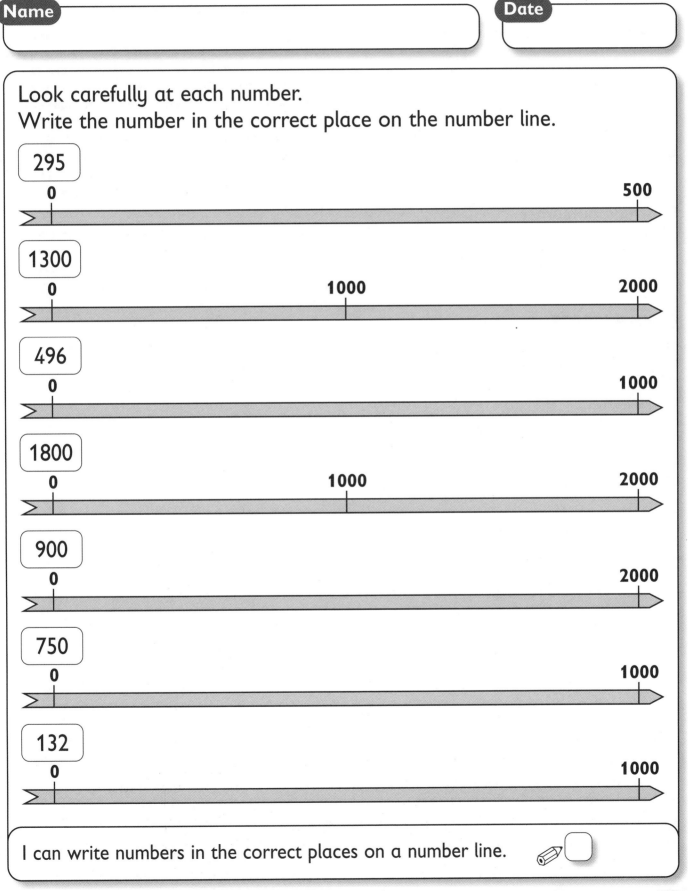

| 295 |
| 0   500 |

| 1300 |
| 0   1000   2000 |

| 496 |
| 0   1000 |

| 1800 |
| 0   1000   2000 |

| 900 |
| 0   2000 |

| 750 |
| 0   1000 |

| 132 |
| 0   1000 |

I can write numbers in the correct places on a number line.

Count on from and back to 0 in single-digit steps

Building on previous learning

Before starting this unit check that the children can already:

- read and write two-digit and three-digit numbers in figures and words.

Learning objectives

Objective 1: Count on from and back to zero in twos, threes, fours, fives and sixes.

Learning outcomes

The children will be able to:

- count on from zero in twos, threes, fours, fives and sixes.
- count back to zero in twos, threes, fours, fives and sixes.

Success criteria

The children have a **secure** level of attainment in relation to Objective 1 if the following questions can be answered with a 'yes'.

Can the children...

... count on orally from zero in two, threes, fours, fives and sixes?

... count back to zero orally from a given start point?

... continue the written sequences shown on the Assessment sheet?

Administering the assessment

Working with a small group of children, ask each child to take turns in counting on from zero in twos. You may like to ask one child to start the sequence then let another take over, then another child, etc. As they work you will need to assess how confidently they are following the sequential pattern. Now ask them to count in threes, fours, fives or sixes. If you still need further evidence you could ask them to count in sevens, eights or nines. Once the children have counted on successfully, ask them to count back in twos from 30; in threes from 39; in fours from 48; in fives from 100; in sixes from 66.

For written evidence ask the children to complete the sequences that are started on the Assessment sheet. As part of the learning experience, encourage the children to notice the common multiples e.g. 30 is in the fives sequence **and** the sixes sequence, etc.

(This assessment will also provide evidence for assessing strand 1, Using and applying mathematics: Identify patterns and relationships involving numbers.)

Count on from and back to 0 in single-digit steps

Name

Date

Look carefully at each number sequence.
Write three extra numbers for each sequence.

0, 2, 4, 6, 8, 10, ⬚ , ⬚ , ⬚ .....

0, 3, 6, 9, 12, 15, ⬚ , ⬚ , ⬚ .....

0, 4, 8, 12, 16, 20, 24, 28, ⬚ , ⬚ , ⬚ .....

0, 5, 10, 15, 20, 2, ⬚ , ⬚ , ⬚ .....

0, 6, 12, 18, ⬚ , ⬚ , ⬚ .....

24, 20, 16, 12, ⬚ , ⬚ , ⬚ .....

36, 30, 24, 18, ⬚ , ⬚ , ⬚ .....

12, 10, 8, 6, ⬚ , ⬚ , ⬚ .....

30, 25, 20, 15, ⬚ , ⬚ , ⬚ .....

18, 15, 12, 9, ⬚ , ⬚ , ⬚ .....

I can count on from 0 in single-digit steps. ⬚

I can count back to 0 in single-digit steps. ⬚

I can continue sequences involving adding or subtracting in single-digit steps. ⬚

Count on from and back to 0 in multiples of 10

Building on previous learning

Before starting this unit check that the children can already:

- read and write two-digit and three-digit numbers in figures and words.

Learning objectives

Objective 1: Count on from and back to zero in tens, twenties, thirties and fifties.

Learning outcomes

The children will be able to:

- count on from zero in tens, twenties, thirties and fifties.
- count back to zero in tens, twenties, thirties and fifties.

Success criteria

The children have a **secure** level of attainment in relation to Objective 1 if the following question can be answered with a 'yes'.

Can the children…

… count on orally from zero in tens, twenties, thirties or fifties?

… count back to zero orally from a given start point?

… continue the written sequences shown on the Assessment sheet?

Administering the assessment

Working with a small group of children, ask each child to take turns in counting on from zero in tens, perhaps as far as 300 or 400. You may like to ask one child to start the sequence then let another take over, then another child, etc. As they work you will need to assess how confidently they are following the sequential pattern. Now ask them to count in twenties, thirties or fifties. If you still need further evidence you could ask them to count in forties. Once the children have counted on successfully, ask them to count back in tens from 300; in twenties from 200; in thirties from 300; in fifties from 500.

For written evidence ask the children to complete the sequences that are started on the Assessment sheet. As part of the learning experience, encourage the children to notice the common multiples e.g. 100 and 200 are all in the tens, twenties and fifties sequences, 300 is in the sequences for the tens, twenties, thirties and fifties, etc.

(This assessment will also provide evidence for assessing strand 1, Using and applying mathematics: Identify patterns and relationships involving numbers.)

Count on from and back to 0 in multiples of 10

Name

Date

Look carefully at each number sequence.
Write four extra numbers for each sequence.

0, 10, 20, 30, 40, ⬚ , ⬚ , ⬚ , ⬚ .....

0, 20, 40, 60, 80, 100, 120, 140, ⬚ , ⬚ , ⬚ , ⬚ .....

0, 30, 60, 90, 120, ⬚ , ⬚ , ⬚ , ⬚ .....

0, 50, 100, 150, 200, ⬚ , ⬚ , ⬚ , ⬚ .....

450, 400, 350, 300, 250, 200, ⬚ , ⬚ , ⬚ , ⬚ .....

200, 180, 160, 140, 120, 100, 80, ⬚ , ⬚ , ⬚ , ⬚ .....

90, 80, 70, 60, 50, 40, ⬚ , ⬚ , ⬚ , ⬚ .....

210, 180, 150, 120, ⬚ , ⬚ , ⬚ , ⬚ .....

I can count on from 0 in multiples of 10. ⬚

I can count back to 0 in multiples of 10. ⬚

I can continue sequences involving adding or subtracting in multiples of 10. ⬚

Partition three-digit numbers into multiples of 100, 10 and 1 in different ways

Building on previous learning

Before starting this unit check that the children can already:

- read and write two-digit and three-digit numbers in figures and words.
- partition two-digit units in different ways including into multiples of 10 and 1.

Learning objectives

Objective 1: Partition three-digit numbers into multiples of 100, 10 and 1.

Learning outcomes

The children will be able to:

- partition any three-digit number into multiples of 100, 10 and 1 in a variety of ways.

Success criteria

The children have a **secure** level of attainment in relation to Objective 1 if the following question can be answered with a 'yes'.

Can the children…

… partition the numbers shown on the Assessment sheet in three different ways, confidently and quickly?

Administering the assessment

The ability to partition numbers helps chilldren to understand other mathematical processes, particularly the process of subtraction by decomposition. The framework specifies that the children should be able to partition three-digit numbers into multiples of 100, 10 and 1 in different ways e.g. a number such as 357 could be partitioned into:

300 + 50 + 7
or 200 + 150 + 7
or 250 + 100 + 7
or 300 + 40 + 17
or 200 + 140 + 17, etc.

You may like to show the pupils this example before asking them to complete the Assessment sheet. Some pupils may have difficulty in reading the text on the sheet but are capable of completing the mathematics. Help these pupils read the instructions, encouraging them to discuss the mathematical processes. Some schools use the term 'ones' rather than 'units' so ensure that the pupils understand that 'units' and 'ones' mean the same.

(This assessment will also provide evidence for assessing strand 1, Using and applying mathematics: Solve one-step and two-step problems involving numbers, choosing and carrying out appropriate calculations; Identify patterns and relationships involving numbers.)

Andrew Brodie: Ten Minute Maths Assessments ages 7–8 © A&C Black 2009

Partition three-digit numbers into multiples of 100, 10 and 1 in different ways

Name

Date

Look at this number: 492

We can split this number into hundreds, tens and units in lots of ways. Here are three examples of how the number could be split:

$$400 + 90 + 2 \qquad 300 + 190 + 2 \qquad 400 + 80 + 12$$

Look carefully at each number. Split the number into hundreds, tens and units in three different ways.

259

563

829

942

607

314

I can find different ways to partition numbers into hundreds, tens and units.

Andrew Brodie: Ten Minute Maths Assessments ages 7–8 © A&C Black 2009

Round two-digit numbers or three-digit numbers to the nearest 10

Building on previous learning

Before starting this unit check that the children can already:
- read, write and order whole numbers to at least 1000 and position them on a number line.
- recognise multiples of 5 and 10.
- partition three-digit numbers into multiples of 100, 10 and 1 in different ways.

Learning objectives

Objective 1: Round two-digit numbers or three-digit numbers to the nearest 10.

Learning outcomes

The children will be able to:
- round up or down to the nearest multiple of 10.
- round up to the nearest 10 from a multiple of 5.

Success criteria

The children have a **secure** level of attainment in relation to Objective 1 if the following questions can be answered with a 'yes'.

Can the children recognise that numbers such as…
- … 67, 469, 18 and 566 can be rounded up to the nearest multiple of 10 to give an approximation?
- … 82, 691, 34 and 373 can be rounded down to the nearest multiple of 10 to give an approximation?
- … 55, 165, 75 and 625 can be rounded up to the nearest multiple of 10 to give an approximation?

Administering the assessment

● Track 2   Ideally the children should work in a small group with an adult. Ensure that they understand the tasks and why we may need to approximate to the nearest 10. They need to be aware of the fact that we always round *up* from multiples of 5. For the first part of the assessment the children have to write approximations of numbers on the sheet. The second part of the assessment involves the use of the CD, with the following text:

Find box a. Round 342 to the nearest ten and write it in box a.
Round 267 to the nearest ten and write it in box b.
Round 189 to the nearest ten and write it in box c.
Round 571 to the nearest ten and write it in box d.
Round 655 to the nearest ten and write it in box e.
Round 785 to the nearest ten and write it in box f.

(This assessment will also provide evidence for assessing strand 1, Using and applying mathematics: Solve one-step problems involving numbers; Follow a line of enquiry by deciding what information is important; Identify patterns and relationships involving numbers.)

Round two-digit numbers or three-digit numbers to the nearest 10

Name

Date

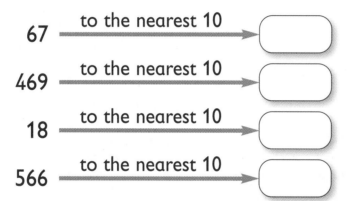

There are 48 ants in the picture.
We could say that there are **about** 50 ants.
We say that 48 rounded to the nearest 10 is 50.

Round these numbers to the nearest 10.

67 ——— to the nearest 10 ———▶ ☐

469 ——— to the nearest 10 ———▶ ☐

18 ——— to the nearest 10 ———▶ ☐

566 ——— to the nearest 10 ———▶ ☐

Now try these.

82 ——— to the nearest 10 ———▶ ☐

691 ——— to the nearest 10 ———▶ ☐

34 ——— to the nearest 10 ———▶ ☐

373 ——— to the nearest 10 ———▶ ☐

Now try these.

55 ——— to the nearest 10 ———▶ ☐

165 ——— to the nearest 10 ———▶ ☐

75 ——— to the nearest 10 ———▶ ☐

625 ——— to the nearest 10 ———▶ ☐

Listen carefully to the CD or your teacher.

a ☐ b ☐ c ☐ d ☐ e ☐ f ☐

I can round two-digit numbers and three-digit numbers to the nearest 10. ☐

Andrew Brodie: Ten Minute Maths Assessments ages 7–8 © A&C Black 2009

Round two-digit numbers or three-digit numbers to the nearest 100

Building on previous learning

Before starting this unit check that the children can already:
- read, write and order whole numbers to at least 1000 and position them on a number line.
- recognise multiples of 5 and 10.
- partition three-digit numbers into multiples of 100, 10 and 1 in different ways.
- round two-digit numbers to the nearest 10.

Learning objectives

Objective 1: Round two-digit numbers or three-digit numbers to the nearest 100.

Learning outcomes

The children will be able to:
- round up or down to the nearest multiple of 100.
- round up to the nearest 100 from a multiple of 50.

Success criteria

The children have a **secure** level of attainment in relation to Objective 1 if the following questions can be answered with a 'yes'.

Can the children recognise that numbers such as...
... 79, 580, 358, 992 and 561 can be rounded up to the nearest multiple of 100 to give an approximation?
... 123, 617, 549, 802 and 932 can be rounded down to the nearest multiple of 100 to give an approximation?
... 150, 350, 650 and 950 can be rounded up to the nearest multiple of 100 to give an approximation?

Administering the assessment

⊙ Track 3 Ideally the children should work in a small group with an adult. Ensure that each child understands the tasks and why we may need to approximate to the nearest 100. The children need to be aware that, when they are rounding to the nearest 100, the *tens* digit is more important than the *units* digit. They will also need to know that they always round *up* from multiples of 50. For the first part of the assessment the children have to write approximations of the numbers on the sheet and can use the number line as a visual aid. The second part of the assessment involves the use of the CD, with the following text:

Find box a. Round 140 to the nearest 100 and write it in box a.
Round 870 to the nearest 100 and write it in box b.
Round 511 to the nearest 100 and write it in box c.
Round 750 to the nearest 100 and write it in box d.
Round 252 to the nearest 100 and write it in box e.
Round 614 to the nearest 100 and write it in box f.

(This assessment will also provide evidence for assessing strand 1, Using and applying mathematics: Solve one-step problems involving numbers; Follow a line of enquiry by deciding what information is important; Identify patterns and relationships involving numbers.)

Round two-digit numbers or three-digit numbers to the nearest 100

Name

Date

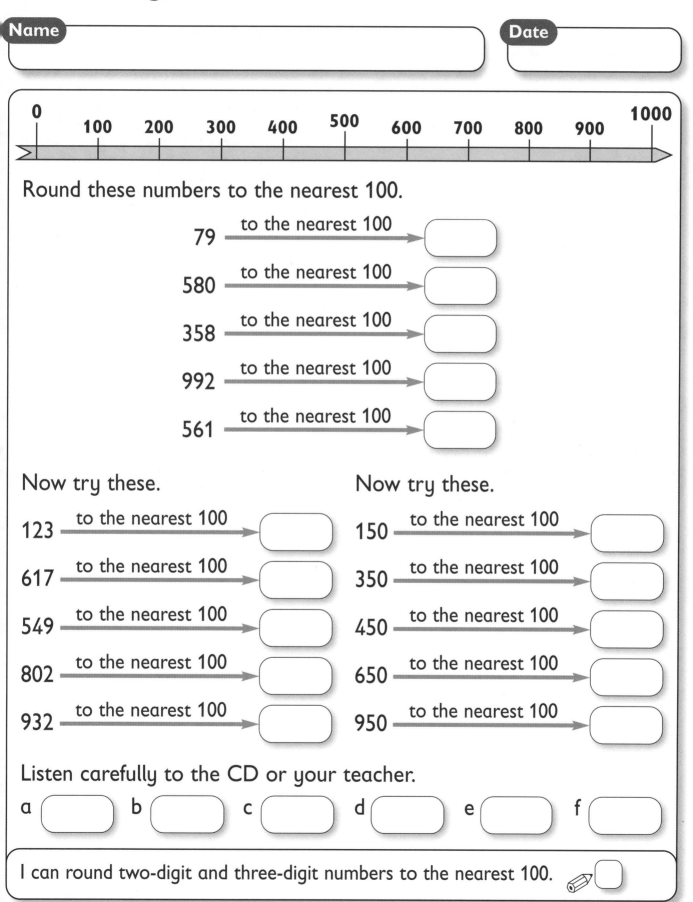

0   100   200   300   400   500   600   700   800   900   1000

Round these numbers to the nearest 100.

79 — to the nearest 100 →

580 — to the nearest 100 →

358 — to the nearest 100 →

992 — to the nearest 100 →

561 — to the nearest 100 →

Now try these.

123 — to the nearest 100 →

617 — to the nearest 100 →

549 — to the nearest 100 →

802 — to the nearest 100 →

932 — to the nearest 100 →

Now try these.

150 — to the nearest 100 →

350 — to the nearest 100 →

450 — to the nearest 100 →

650 — to the nearest 100 →

950 — to the nearest 100 →

Listen carefully to the CD or your teacher.

a   b   c   d   e   f

I can round two-digit and three-digit numbers to the nearest 100.

Round two-digit numbers or three-digit numbers to the nearest 10 or 100 (and give estimates for their sums and differences)

Building on previous learning

Before starting this unit check that the children can already:
- partition three-digit numbers into multiples of 100, 10 and 1 in different ways.
- round two-digit numbers or three-digit numbers to the nearest 10 or 100.

Learning objectives

Objective 1: Round two-digit numbers or three-digit numbers to the nearest 10 or 100 and give estimates for their sums and differences.

Learning outcomes

The children will be able to:
- use their ability to round two-digit numbers or three-digit numbers to the nearest 10 or 100 when making estimates for answers to questions involving addition or subtraction.

Success criteria

The children have a **secure** level of attainment in relation to Objective 1 if the following question can be answered with a 'yes'.

Can the children…

… make appropriate approximations of the numbers provided to enable them to find estimates of their sums or differences?

Administering the assessment

● Track 4 Ideally the children should work in a small group with an adult. The assessment relies on the use of the CD for a timed test where the children are given ten seconds to answer each question. The purpose of the limited time is to encourage the pupils to make appropriate approximations for each answer before they actually add them or find the difference. If there is no time limit the children will attempt to work out the exact answer, which is not the purpose of the task. Ensure that the children have looked at the Assessment sheet before they start the test, to enable them to understand that their answers will be written in the boxes provided. The practice question will help with this. This is the script for the CD if you decide to dictate the questions.

I will say each question twice then you will have ten seconds to answer it.
Practice question. Look at the two numbers, 78 and 26. Round each of these to the nearest 10 then add to find the approximate sum of 78 and 26. Write your answer in the space provided.
Question 1: Roughly how much is the total of 168 and 59? (230)
Question 2: Find the approximate answer to 692 plus 585. (1300)
Question 3: Approximately how much is the total of 487 and 302? (800)
Question 4: Roughly how much is the difference between 192 and 48? (140)
Question 5: Approximately how much more than 217 is 942? (700)
Question 6: Find the approximate answer to 708 minus 498. (200)
Question 7: Roughly how much is 865 plus 787? (1700)
Question 8: Approximately how much is 999 minus 306? (700)

Appropriate approximate answers are shown above in brackets. However, some children will be able to produce even closer approximations or possibly the exact answers for some of the questions and should be given credit for these answers, provided they have completed the questions in the time allowed.

(This assessment will also provide evidence for assessing strand 1, Using and applying mathematics: Solve one-step problems involving numbers; Follow a line of enquiry by deciding what information is important; Identify patterns and relationships involving numbers.)

Round two-digit numbers or three-digit numbers to the nearest 10 or 100

Name

Date

Practice question. 78   26   ⬭

1. ⬭   168   59

2. ⬭   692   585

3. ⬭   487   302

4. ⬭   192   48

5. ⬭   217   942

6. ⬭   708   498

7. ⬭   865   787

8. ⬭   999   306

I can round two-digit and three-digit numbers to the nearest 10 or 100 and use these approximations to find estimated answers to additions and subtractions.

Read and write proper fractions

Building on previous learning

Before starting this unit check that the children can already:

- use the vocabulary of halves and quarters in context, e.g. when discussing food items such as cakes, pizzas, apples, bars of chocolate, etc.
- find one half, one quarter and three quarters of shapes and sets of objects.

Learning objectives

Objective 1: Read and write proper fractions e.g. $\frac{3}{7}$, $\frac{9}{10}$, interpreting the denominator as the parts of a whole and the numerator as the number of parts.

Learning outcomes

The children will be able to:

- read and write proper fractions.

Success criteria

The children have a **secure** level of attainment in relation to Objective 1 if the following questions can be answered with a 'yes'.

Can the children…
… match shaded circles to fractions provided?
… write the correct fractions for shaded circles provided?
… colour circles to represent the fractions provided?

Administering the assessment

Ideally the children should work in a small group with an adult. Ensure that each child understands the tasks on the Assessment sheet, understanding that the circles are referred to as 'fraction cakes'.

(This assessment will also provide evidence for assessing strand 1, Using and applying mathematics: Represent the information in a puzzle or problem using numbers, images or diagrams; Identify patterns and relationships involving numbers; Desribe and explain methods, choices and solutions to puzzles and problems, orally and in writing, using pictures and diagrams.)

Andrew Brodie: Ten Minute Maths Assessments ages 7–8 © A&C Black 2009

Read and write proper fractions

Name

Date

Match the fraction cakes to the fractions.
The first one has been done for you.

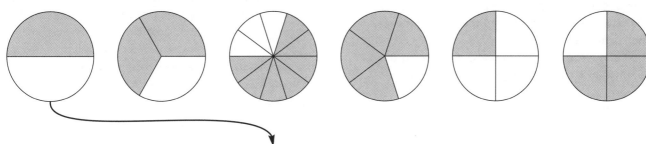

$$\frac{1}{4} \qquad \frac{3}{4} \qquad \frac{1}{2} \qquad \frac{2}{3} \qquad \frac{4}{5} \qquad \frac{7}{10}$$

Write the correct fraction for each fraction cake.

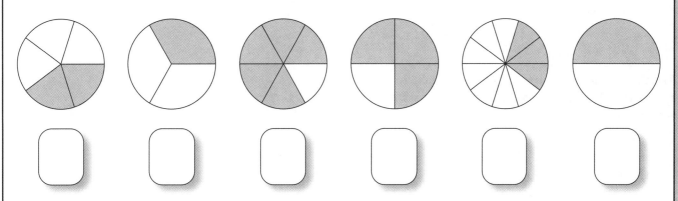

Shade the cakes to show the fractions.

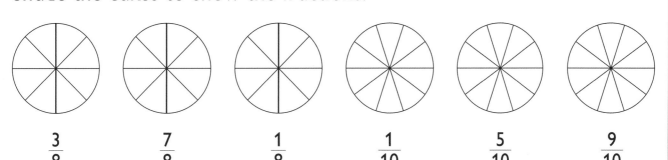

$$\frac{3}{8} \qquad \frac{7}{8} \qquad \frac{1}{8} \qquad \frac{1}{10} \qquad \frac{5}{10} \qquad \frac{9}{10}$$

I can read and write proper fractions, interpreting the denominator as the parts of a whole and the numerator as the number of parts.

Andrew Brodie: Ten Minute Maths Assessments ages 7–8 © A&C Black 2009

Identify and estimate fractions of shapes

Building on previous learning

Before starting this unit check that the children can already:

- use the vocabulary of halves and quarters in context, e.g. when discussing food items such as cakes, pizzas, apples, bars of chocolate, etc.
- find one half, one quarter and three quarters of shapes and sets of objects.
- read and write proper fractions, interpreting the denominator as the parts of a whole and the numerator as the number of parts.

Learning objectives

Objective 1: Identify and estimate fractions of shapes.

Learning outcomes

The children will be able to:

- identify fractions of shapes.
- estimate fractions of shapes by colouring.

Success criteria

The children have a **secure** level of attainment in relation to Objective 1 if the following questions can be answered with a 'yes'.

Can the children...

... correctly identify the fraction of each shape that is shaded?

... colour appropriate parts of each shape to represent the fraction provided?

Administering the assessment

Ideally the children should work in a small group with an adult. Ensure that each child understands the tasks on the Assessment sheet.

(This assessment will also provide evidence for assessing strand 1, Using and applying mathematics: Represent the information in a puzzle or problem using numbers, images or diagrams; Identify patterns and relationships involving numbers; Desribe and explain methods, choices and solutions to puzzles and problems, orally and in writing, using pictures and diagrams.)

Andrew Brodie: Ten Minute Maths Assessments ages 7–8 © A&C Black 2009

Identify and estimate fractions of shapes

Name

Date

Look at each shape. For each shape write down the fraction that is shaded and the fraction that is unshaded.

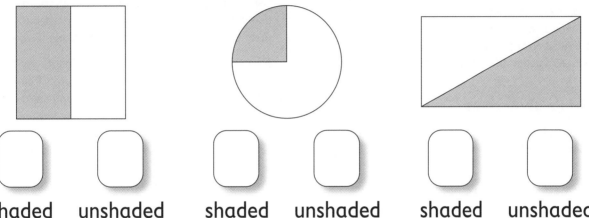

shaded   unshaded   shaded   unshaded   shaded   unshaded

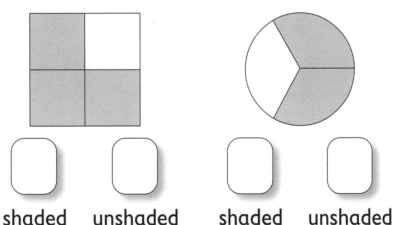

shaded   unshaded   shaded   unshaded

Look at each shape. Colour part of each shape to show the fraction.

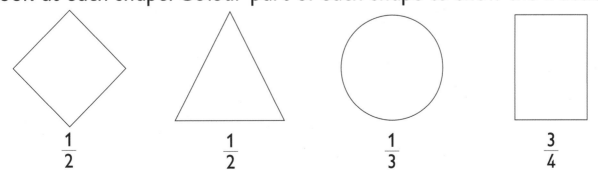

$\frac{1}{2}$ $\frac{1}{2}$ $\frac{1}{3}$ $\frac{3}{4}$

I can identify and estimate fractions of shapes.

Use diagrams to compare fractions and establish equivalents

Building on previous learning

Before starting this unit check that the children can already:
- use the vocabulary of halves and quarters in context, e.g. when discussing food items such as cakes, pizzas, apples, bars of chocolate, etc.
- find one half, one quarter and three quarters of shapes and sets of objects.
- read and write proper fractions, interpreting the denominator as the parts of a whole and the numerator as the number of parts.
- identify and estimate fractions of shapes.

Learning objectives

Objective 1: Use diagrams to compare fractions and establish equivalents.

Learning outcomes

The children will be able to:
- discuss 'fraction cakes' to make comparisons.
- identify which 'fraction cakes' represent the same amount.

Success criteria

The children have a **secure** level of attainment in relation to Objective 1 if the following questions can be answered with a 'yes'.

Can the children…
- … discuss the diagrams on the Assessment sheet, making comparisons between amounts shaded?
- … find three 'fraction cakes' that are equivalent to $\frac{1}{2}$ and one that is equivalent to $\frac{3}{4}$?

Administering the assessment

Ideally the children should work in a small group with an adult. Ask the children to look carefully at the 'fraction cakes' and to tell you what fraction of each cake is shaded, before they write the fractions in the appropriate places. Then ask questions such as: Which is bigger, $\frac{1}{2}$ or $\frac{3}{4}$? Which is smaller, $\frac{1}{3}$ or $\frac{1}{4}$? Which is bigger, $\frac{2}{3}$ or $\frac{3}{4}$?

Ask the children to identify a fraction that is the same amount as $\frac{1}{4}$. They should be able to point out $\frac{2}{8}$. Now ask them to complete the final two tasks on the sheet.

(This assessment will also provide evidence for assessing strand 1, Using and applying mathematics: Represent the information in a puzzle or problem using numbers, images or diagrams; Identify patterns and relationships involving numbers; Describe and explain methods, choices and solutions to puzzles and problems, orally and in writing, using pictures and diagrams.)

Andrew Brodie: Ten Minute Maths Assessments ages 7–8 © A&C Black 2009

Use diagrams to compare fractions and establish equivalents

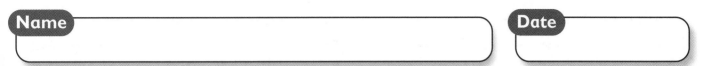

Name

Date

Look at each fraction cake. Write the fraction shaded under each one.

a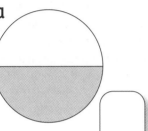

b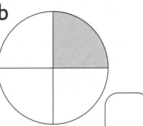

c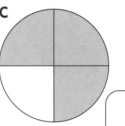

d

e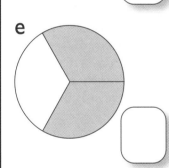

f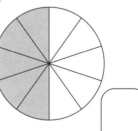

g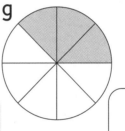

h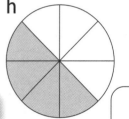

i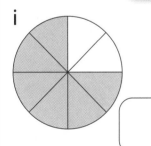

j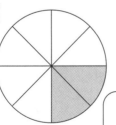

k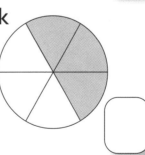

The first fraction cake shows $\frac{1}{2}$.
Can you find three other fraction cakes that
have the same amount shaded as $\frac{1}{2}$?

One fraction cake shows $\frac{3}{4}$. Can you find another
fraction cake that has the same amount shaded as $\frac{3}{4}$?

I can use diagrams to compare fractions.

I can use diagrams to establish equivalent fractions.

Andrew Brodie: Ten Minute Maths Assessments ages 7–8 © A&C Black 2009

Derive all addition facts for each number to 20

Building on previous learning

Before starting this unit check that the children can already:
- derive and recall all addition and subtraction facts for each number to at least 10.
- calculate the value of an unknown in a number sentence.

Learning objectives

Objective 1: Derive all addition facts for each number to 20.

Learning outcomes

The children will be able to:
- derive all addition facts for each number to 20.

Success criteria

The children have a **secure** level of attainment in relation to Objective 1 if the following question can be answered with a 'yes'.

Can the children...
... complete all the tasks on the Assessment sheet, confidently and independently?

Administering the assessment

Discuss the example with the children, ensuring that they understand the addition sentences and know that they are only working with whole numbers.

Look at the first set of questions with the children to assess whether they are able to calculate the value of an unknown in a number sentence. Not all numbers to 20 have been included but if you feel that further evidence would be useful you could ask the children to write addition sentences for some of the numbers that have not been used. This assessment is based on *deriving* the addition facts. To establish whether the pupils can *recall* these facts you will need to use Assessment sheet 13 with the CD.

(This assessment will also provide evidence for assessing strand 1, Using and applying mathematics: Follow a line of enquiry by deciding what information is important; make and use lists, tables and graphs to organise and interpret the information; Identify patterns and relationships involving numbers; Desribe and explain methods, choices and solutions to puzzles and problems, orally and in writing, using pictures and diagrams.)

Derive all addition facts for each number to 20

There are twelve pound coins. Here are some addition sentences that make 12.

12 + 0 = 12   11 + 1 = 12   10 + 2 = 12   9 + 3 = 12

Write nine more addition sentences for 12.

[ ] [ ] [ ] [ ] [ ]

[ ] [ ] [ ] [ ]

Complete these addition sentences to make 14.

14 + [ ] = 14   3 + [ ] = 14   7 + [ ] = 14

9 + [ ] = 14   0 + [ ] = 14

For each number find all the addition facts.

16	19	13
15 + 1		

I can find addition facts for each number to 20.

Recall all addition facts for each number to 20

Building on previous learning

Before starting this unit check that the children can already:
- derive and recall all addition and subtraction facts for each number to at least 10.

Learning objectives

Objective 1: Recall all addition facts for each number to 20.

Learning outcomes

The children will be able to:
- recall rapidly all addition facts for each number to 20.

Success criteria

The children have a **secure** level of attainment in relation to Objective 1 if the following question can be answered with a 'yes'.

Can the children…

… respond quickly and accurately to questions such as 'What number must be added to fourteen to make nineteen?'

Administering the assessment

⊙ Track 5 Ideally the children should work in a small group with an adult. The assessment relies on the use of the CD for a timed test where the children are given five seconds to answer each question. The purpose of the limited time is to ensure that the children can *recall* the facts. Ensure that the children have looked at the Assessment sheet before they start the test, to enable them to see that they need to write their answers in the boxes provided. The practice question will help with this. This is the script for the CD if you decide to dictate the questions.

I will say each question twice then you will have five seconds to answer it.
Practice question. Look at the number 13. What number must be added to 13 to make 16? Write your answer in the space provided.
Question 1: What number must be added to 8 to make 15?
Question 2: What number must be added to 7 to make 19?
Question 3: What number must be added to 9 to make 17?
Question 4: What number must be added to 12 to make 18?
Question 5: What number must be added to 13 to make 20?
Question 6: What number must be added to 8 to make 16?
Question 7: What number must be added to 6 to make 15?
Question 8: What number must be added to 5 to make 13?
Question 9: What is 8 add 4?
Question 10: What is the total of 7 and 9?
Question 11: How much is 6 and 8 altogether?
Question 12: What is the sum of 9 and 8?
Question 13: What is the total of 8 and 7?
Question 14: What is 10 add 9?
Question 15: How much is 9 and 4 altogether?

(This assessment will also provide evidence for assessing strand 1, Using and applying mathematics: Follow a line of enquiry by deciding what information is important; make and use lists, tables and graphs to organise and interpret the information; Identify patterns and relationships involving numbers; Desribe and explain methods, choices and solutions to puzzles and problems, orally and in writing, using pictures and diagrams.)

Andrew Brodie: Ten Minute Maths Assessments ages 7–8 © A&C Black 2009

Recall all addition facts for each number to 20

Name

Date

Listen carefully to the CD or your teacher.

Practice question. 13 ( )

1. ( ) 8

2. ( ) 7

3. ( ) 9

4. ( ) 12

5. ( ) 13

6. ( ) 8

7. ( ) 6

8. ( ) 5

9. ( ) 8, 4

10. ( ) 7, 9

11. ( ) 6, 8

12. ( ) 9, 8

13. ( ) 8, 7

14. ( ) 10, 9

15. ( ) 9, 4

I can recall addition facts for each number to 20. ( )

Andrew Brodie: Ten Minute Maths Assessments ages 7–8 © A&C Black 2009

Derive all subtraction facts for each number to 20

Building on previous learning

Before starting this unit check that the children can already:
- derive and recall all addition and subtraction facts for each number to at least 10.

Learning objectives

Objective 1: Derive all subtraction facts for each number to 20.

Learning outcomes

The children will be able to:
- derive all subtraction facts for each number to 20.

Success criteria

The children have a **secure** level of attainment in relation to Objective 1 if the following question can be answered with a 'yes'.

Can the children…
… complete all the tasks on the Assessment sheet, confidently and independently?

Administering the assessment

Discuss the example with the children, ensuring that they understand the subtraction sentences and know that only whole numbers are involved. Not all numbers to 20 have been included. If you feel that additional evidence is required you could ask the children to write subtraction sentences for some of the numbers that have not been used. This assessment is based on a child's ability to *derive* the subtraction facts. To establish whether the children can *recall* these facts you will need to use Assessment sheet 15 with the CD.

(This assessment will also provide evidence for assessing strand 1, Using and applying mathematics: Follow a line of enquiry by deciding what information is important; make and use lists, tables and graphs to organise and interpret the information; Identify patterns and relationships involving numbers; Desribe and explain methods, choices and solutions to puzzles and problems, orally and in writing, using pictures and diagrams.)

Derive all subtraction facts for each number to 20

Name

Date

Here are some subtraction sentences from 15.

15 − 15 = 0   15 − 14 = 1   15 − 13 = 2
15 − 12 = 3   15 − 11 = 4   15 − 10 = 5

Write 10 more subtraction sentences from 15.

For each number find all the subtraction facts.

20

20 − 0 = 20

12

16

I can find subtraction facts for each number to 20.

Andrew Brodie: Ten Minute Maths Assessments ages 7–8 © A&C Black 2009

Recall all subtraction facts for each number to 20

Building on previous learning

Before starting this unit check that the children can already:
- derive and recall all addition and subtraction facts for each number to at least 10.

Learning objectives

Objective 1: Recall all subtraction facts for each number to 20.

Learning outcomes

The children will be able to:
- recall rapidly all subtraction facts for each number to 20.

Success criteria

The children have a **secure** level of attainment in relation to Objective 1 if the following question can be answered with a 'yes'.

Can the children...
... respond quickly and accurately to questions such as '19 subtract 12?'

Administering the assessment

🔵 Track 6 Ideally the children should work in a small group with an adult. The assessment relies on the use of the CD for a timed test where the children are given five seconds to answer each question. The purpose of the limited time is to ensure that the children can *recall* the facts. Ensure that the children have looked at the Assessment sheet before they start the test to enable them to see that they need to write their answers in the boxes provided. The practice question will help with this. This is the script for the CD if you decide to dictate the questions.

I will say each question twice then you will have five seconds to answer it.
Practice question. What is the difference between 16 and 11?
Question 1: What is the difference between 12 and 7?
Question 2: What is the difference between 18 and 14?
Question 3: What is the difference between 10 and 3?
Question 4: What is the difference between 20 and 12?
Question 5: 14 subtract 6
Question 6: 17 subtract 5
Question 7: 19 subtract 8
Question 8: 11 subtract 5
Question 9: 12 subtract 4
Question 10: 13 take 5
Question 11: 15 take 9
Question 12: 18 take 6
Question 13: 16 minus 9
Question 14: 14 minus 8
Question 15: 17 minus 4
Question 16: How many fewer is 12 than 17?
Question 17: How many fewer is 12 than 19?
Question 18: How many fewer is 6 than 15?
Question 19: How many fewer is 9 than 16?
Question 20: How many fewer is 8 than 17?

(This assessment will also provide evidence for assessing strand 1, Using and applying mathematics: Follow a line of enquiry by deciding what information is important; make and use lists, tables and graphs to organise and interpret the information; Identify patterns and relationships involving numbers; Desribe and explain methods, choices and solutions to puzzles and problems, orally and in writing, using pictures and diagrams.)

Recall all subtraction facts for each number to 20

Name

Date

Listen carefully to the CD or your teacher.

Practice question. 16   11   ( )

1. ( )	12, 7	11. ( )	15, 9
2. ( )	18, 14	12. ( )	18, 6
3. ( )	10, 3	13. ( )	16, 9
4. ( )	20, 12	14. ( )	14, 8
5. ( )	14, 6	15. ( )	17, 4
6. ( )	17, 5	16. ( )	12, 17
7. ( )	19, 8	17. ( )	12, 19
8. ( )	11, 5	18. ( )	6, 15
9. ( )	12, 4	19. ( )	9, 16
10. ( )	13, 5	20. ( )	8, 17

I can recall subtraction facts for each number to 20. ( )

Andrew Brodie: Ten Minute Maths Assessments ages 7–8 © A&C Black 2009

Derive and recall sums and differences of multiples of 10

Building on previous learning

Before starting this unit check that the children can already:

- derive and recall all addition and subtraction facts for each number to 20.

Learning objectives

Objective 1: Derive and recall sums and differences of multiples of 10.

Learning outcomes

The children will be able to:

- recall sums and differences of multiples of 10.

Success criteria

The children have a **secure** level of attainment in relation to Objective 1 if the following question can be answered with a 'yes'.

Can the children…

… respond quickly and accurately to questions such as 'What is the total of 50 and 70?' 'What is the difference between 90 and 40?'

Administering the assessment

● Track 7   Ideally the children should work in a small group with an adult. At this stage the children have had considerable experience in deriving and recalling addition and subtraction facts and should be able to *derive* the sums and differences of multiples of 10 confidently and quickly. This assessment is based on whether children can *recall* the sums and differences of multiples of 10. The assessment relies on the CD for a timed test where the children are given ten seconds to answer each question. The purpose of the limited time is to ensure that the children have some thinking time but can then *recall* the facts. Ensure that the children have looked at the Assessment sheet before they start the test to enable them to see that they need to write their answers in the boxes provided. The practice question will help with this. This is the script for the CD if you decide to dictate the questions.

I will say each question twice then you will have ten seconds to answer it.
Practice question: What is the total of 40 and 30?
Question 1: What is the difference between 80 and 50?
Question 2: What is 70 add 30?
Question 3: What is the sum of 90 and 60?
Question 4: What is the difference between 100 and 20?
Question 5: 90 add 80
Question 6: 110 subtract 40
Question 7: 60 minus 30
Question 8: What number is double 80?
Question 9: What number is half of 120?
Question 10: 140 take 60
Question 11: 150 minus 90
Question 12: 150 plus 50
Question 13: 80 plus 60
Question 14: What is the total of 170 and 40?
Question 15: What is the difference between 160 and 110?
Question 16: What is the sum of 180 and 90?
Question 17: What number is double 90?
Question 18: 90 plus 70
Question 19: 120 subtract 50
Question 20: 210 minus 70

(This assessment will also provide evidence for assessing strand 1, Using and applying mathematics: Follow a line of enquiry by deciding what information is important; make and use lists, tables and graphs to organise and interpret the information; Identify patterns and relationships involving numbers; Desribe and explain methods, choices and solutions to puzzles and problems, orally and in writing, using pictures and diagrams.)

Derive and recall sums and differences of multiples of 10

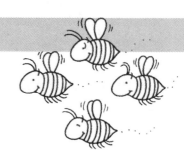

Name

Date

Listen carefully to the CD or your teacher.

Practice question. 40   30

1.	80	50	**11.**	150	90
2.	70	30	**12.**	150	50
3.	90	60	**13.**	80	60
4.	100	20	**14.**	170	40
5.	90	80	**15.**	160	110
6.	110	40	**16.**	180	90
7.	60	30	**17.**	90	
8.	80		**18.**	90	70
9.	120		**19.**	120	50
10.	140	60	**20.**	210	70

I can recall sums and differences of multiples of 10.

Derive and recall number pairs that total 100

Building on previous learning

Before starting this unit check that the children can already:

- derive and recall all addition and subtraction facts for each number to 20.

Learning objectives

Objective 1: Derive and recall number pairs that total 100.

Learning outcomes

The children will be able to:

- recall number pairs that total 100.

Success criteria

The children have a **secure** level of attainment in relation to Objective 1 if the following questions can be answered with a 'yes'.

Can the children…

… respond quickly and accurately to questions such as 'What must be added to 43 to make 100?' 'What is 100 subtract 27?'

Administering the assessment

🔘 Track 8   Ideally the children should work in a small group with an adult. By this stage the pupils have had considerable experience in deriving and recalling addition and subtraction facts and should be able to derive and recall the number pairs that total 100. However, many confident children will subtract a number such as 32 from 100 incorrectly. They are likely to subtract the 30 to reach 70, then they know that 2 from 10 gives 8 so they produce the answer 78 – practice with a number line will overcome this and so a number line is provided on the Assessment sheet. The assessment relies on the CD for a timed test where the children are given ten seconds to answer each question. This allows them enough time to refer to the number line as a prompt if necessary but will test whether they can *recall* the appropriate fact. Ensure that the children have looked at the Assessment sheet before they start the test to enable them to see that they need to write their answers in the boxes provided. The practice question will help with this. This is the script for the CD if you decide to dictate the questions.

I will say each question twice then you will have ten seconds to answer it.
Practice question: What is 100 minus 50?
Question 1: What is 100 subtract 48?
Question 2: What must be added to 43 to make 100?
Question 3: What is the difference between 27 and 100?
Question 4: What is the difference between 100 and 59?
Question 5: 100 take away 67
Question 6: 100 subtract 99
Question 7: How much more is 100 than 45?
Question 8: How many more must I add to 75 sweets to make 100 sweets?
Question 9: What number is half of 100?
Question 10: 100 take 17
Question 11: What number is 84 less than 100?
Question 12: What is the difference between 29 and 100?
Question 13: 100 minus 41
Question 14: What is the total of 64 and 36?
Question 15: What is the difference between 100 and 83?
Question 16: What number is 38 less than 100?
Question 17: What is 100 minus 42?
Question 18: How much must be added to 31 to make 100?
Question 19: What is 100 take 7?
Question 20: 100 take away 76

(This assessment will also provide evidence for assessing strand 1, Using and applying mathematics: Follow a line of enquiry by deciding what information is important; make and use lists, tables and graphs to organise and interpret the information; Identify patterns and relationships involving numbers; Desribe and explain methods, choices and solutions to puzzles and problems, orally and in writing, using pictures and diagrams.)

Derive and recall number pairs that total 100

Name

Date

Listen carefully to the CD or your teacher.

Practice question. 100 50 [ ]

1. [ ]	100	48		11. [ ]	84	100
2. [ ]	43	100		12. [ ]	29	100
3. [ ]	27	100		13. [ ]	100	41
4. [ ]	100	59		14. [ ]	64	36
5. [ ]	100	67		15. [ ]	100	83
6. [ ]	100	99		16. [ ]	38	100
7. [ ]	100	45		17. [ ]	100	42
8. [ ]	75	100		18. [ ]	31	100
9. [ ]	100			19. [ ]	100	7
10. [ ]	100	17		20. [ ]	100	76

I can derive and recall number pairs that total 100. [ ]

Andrew Brodie: Ten Minute Maths Assessments ages 7–8 © A&C Black 2009

Derive and recall multiplication facts for the 2 times table

Building on previous learning

Before starting this unit check that the children can already:

- count on or back in ones, twos, fives and tens and use this knowledge to derive the multiples of 2, 5 and 10 to the tenth multiple.

Learning objectives

Objective 1: Derive multiplication facts for the 2 times table.

Objective 2: Recall multiplication facts for the 2 times table.

(Note that these learning objectives are listed in the framework for Year 3 but are the same as those listed for Year 2 due to the fact that tables need repetition.)

Learning outcomes

The children will be able to:

- derive and recall all multiplication facts for the 2 times table.

Success criteria

The children have a **secure** level of attainment in relation to Objective 1 if the following question can be answered with a 'yes'.

Can the children…

… complete the task on the top half of the Assessment sheet, confidently and independently?

The children have a **secure** level of attainment in relation to Objective 2 if the following question can be answered with a 'yes'.

Can the children…

… respond quickly and accurately to the questions on the CD?

Administering the assessment

⦿ Track 9 Ensure that the children understand the task of writing out the table on the top half of the sheet. They may need to use the array of circles or counting apparatus to help them. Once they have completed the task ask them to fold the sheets and to listen carefully to the CD. They should be able to answer the questions without the need to pause the CD. This is the script for the CD if you decide to dictate the questions.

I will say each question twice then you will have five seconds to answer it.
Question 1: What is 6 times 2?
Question 2: What is 2 multiplied by 3?
Question 3: What is the product of 5 and 2?
Question 4: Multiply 2 by 9
Question 5: 7 times 2
Question 6: 0 times 2
Question 7: What is 10 times 2?
Question 8: 8 times 2
Question 9: What is the product of 1 and 2?
Question 10: What is 4 times 2?

(This assessment will also provide evidence for assessing strand 1, Using and applying mathematics: Identify patterns and relationships involving numbers or shapes.)

Derive and recall multiplication facts for the 2 times table

Name

Date

Write the 2 times table.
It has been started for you.

$1 \times 2 = 2$

$2 \times 2 = 4$

Now fold the paper so that you cannot see the 2 times table.

Listen carefully to the CD or your teacher.

1 [ ] 2 [ ] 3 [ ] 4 [ ] 5 [ ]

6 [ ] 7 [ ] 8 [ ] 9 [ ] 10 [ ]

I can find the multiplication facts for the 2 times table.

I can recall the multiplication facts for the 2 times table.

Derive and recall multiplication facts for the 5 times table

Building on previous learning

Before starting this unit check that the children can already:

- count on or back in ones, twos, fives and tens and use this knowledge to derive the multiples of 2, 5 and 10 to the tenth multiple.

Learning objectives

Objective 1: Derive multiplication facts for the 5 times table.
Objective 2: Recall multiplication facts for the 5 times table.
(Note that these learning objectives are listed in the framework for Year 3 but are the same as those listed for Year 2 due to the fact that tables need repetition.)

Learning outcomes

The children will be able to:

- derive and recall all multiplication facts for the 5 times table.

Success criteria

The children have a **secure** level of attainment in relation to Objective 1 if the following question can be answered with a 'yes'.

Can the children...
... complete the task on the top half of the Assessment sheet, confidently and independently?

The children have a **secure** level of attainment in relation to Objective 2 if the following question can be answered with a 'yes'.

Can the children...
... respond quickly and accurately to the questions on the CD?

Administering the assessment

🔘 Track 10 Ensure that the children understand the task of writing out the table on the top half of the sheet. They may need to use the array of pentagons or counting apparatus to help them. Once they have completed the task ask them to fold the sheets and to listen carefully to the CD. They should be able to answer the questions without the need to pause the CD. This is the script for the CD if you decide to dictate the questions.

I will say each question twice then you will have five seconds to answer it.
Question 1: What is 7 times 5?
Question 2: What is 5 multiplied by 5?
Question 3: What is the product of 5 and 8?
Question 4: Multiply 5 by 2
Question 5: 6 times 5
Question 6: 0 times 5
Question 7: What is 10 times 5?
Question 8: 9 times 5
Question 9: What is the product of 3 and 5?
Question 10: What is 4 times 5?

(This assessment will also provide evidence for assessing strand 1, Using and applying mathematics: Identify patterns and relationships involving numbers or shapes.)

Derive and recall multiplication facts for the 5 times table

Name

Date

Write the 5 times table.
It has been started for you.

1 x 5 = 5

2 x 5 = 10

Now fold the paper so that you cannot see the 5 times table.

Listen carefully to the CD or your teacher.

1 ⬚ 2 ⬚ 3 ⬚ 4 ⬚ 5 ⬚

6 ⬚ 7 ⬚ 8 ⬚ 9 ⬚ 10 ⬚

I can find the multiplication facts for the 5 times table. ⬚

I can recall the multiplication facts for the 5 times table. ⬚

Derive and recall multiplication facts for the 10 times table

Building on previous learning

Before starting this unit check that the children can already:

- count on or back in ones, twos, fives and tens and use this knowledge to derive the multiples of 2, 5 and 10 to the tenth multiple.

Learning objectives

Objective 1: Derive multiplication facts for the 10 times table.

Objective 2: Recall multiplication facts for the 10 times table.

(Note that these learning objectives are listed in the framework for Year 3 but are the same as those listed for Year 2 due to the fact that tables need repetition.)

Learning outcomes

The children will be able to:

- derive and recall all multiplication facts for the 10 times table.

Success criteria

The children have a **secure** level of attainment in relation to Objective 1 if the following question can be answered with a 'yes'.

Can the children…
… complete the task on the top half of the Assessment sheet, confidently and independently?

The children have a **secure** level of attainment in relation to Objective 2 if the following question can be answered with a 'yes'.

Can the children…
… respond quickly and accurately to the questions on the CD?

Administering the assessment

● Track 11 Ensure that the children understand the task of writing out the table on the top half of the page. They may need to use the array of squares or counting apparatus to help them. Once they have completed the task ask them to fold the sheets and to listen carefully to the CD. They should be able to answer the questions without the need to pause the CD. This is the script for the CD if you decide to dictate the questions.

I will say each question twice then you will have five seconds to answer it.
Question 1: What is 10 multiplied by 4?
Question 2: What is 2 times 10?
Question 3: What is the product of 1 and 10?
Question 4: Multiply 10 by 9
Question 5: 8 times 10
Question 6: 10 multiplied by 3
Question 7: What is 6 times 10?
Question 8: 7 times 10
Question 9: What is the product of 5 and 10?
Question 10: What is 10 times 10?

(This assessment will also provide evidence for assessing strand 1, Using and applying mathematics: Identify patterns and relationships involving numbers or shapes.)

Andrew Brodie: Ten Minute Maths Assessments ages 7–8 © A&C Black 2009

Derive and recall multiplication facts for the 10 times table

Name

Date

Write the 10 times table.
It has been started for you.

1 x 10 = 10

2 x 10 = 20

Now fold the paper so that you cannot see the 10 times table.

Listen carefully to the CD or your teacher.

1 ⬜ 2 ⬜ 3 ⬜ 4 ⬜ 5 ⬜

6 ⬜ 7 ⬜ 8 ⬜ 9 ⬜ 10 ⬜

I can find the multiplication facts for the 10 times table.

I can recall the multiplication facts for the 10 times table.

Derive and recall multiplication facts for the 3 times table

Building on previous learning

Before starting this unit check that the children can already:
- derive and recall multiplication facts for the 2 times, 5 times and 10 times tables.

Learning objectives

Objective 1: Derive multiplication facts for the 3 times table.

Objective 2: Recall multiplication facts for the 3 times table.

Learning outcomes

The children will be able to:
- derive and recall all multiplication facts for the 3 times table.

Success criteria

The children have a **secure** level of attainment in relation to Objective 1 if the following question can be answered with a 'yes'.

Can the children…
… complete the task on the top half of the Assessment sheet, confidently and independently?

The children have a **secure** level of attainment in relation to Objective 2 if the following question can be answered with a 'yes'.

Can the children…
… respond quickly and accurately to the questions on the CD?

Administering the assessment

⏺ Track 12 Ensure that the children understand the task of writing out the table on the top half of the page. They may need to use the array of triangles or counting apparatus to help them. Once they have completed the task ask them to fold the sheets and to listen carefully to the CD. They should be able to answer the questions without the need to pause the CD. This is the script for the CD if you decide to dictate the questions.

I will say each question twice then you will have five seconds to answer it.
Question 1: What is 3 multiplied by 7?
Question 2: What is 8 times 3?
Question 3: What is the product of zero and 3?
Question 4: Multiply 3 by 4
Question 5: 6 times 3
Question 6: 3 multiplied by 2
Question 7: What is 3 times 3?
Question 8: 9 times 3
Question 9: What is the product of 5 and 3?
Question 10: What is 10 times 3?

(This assessment will also provide evidence for assessing strand 1, Using and applying mathematics: Identify patterns and relationships involving numbers or shapes.)

Andrew Brodie: Ten Minute Maths Assessments ages 7–8 © A&C Black 2009

Derive and recall multiplication facts for the 3 times table

Name

Date

Write the 3 times table.
It has been started for you.

1 x 3 = 3

2 x 3 = 6

Now fold the paper so that you cannot see the 3 times table.

Listen carefully to the CD or your teacher.

1 ⬚   2 ⬚   3 ⬚   4 ⬚   5 ⬚

6 ⬚   7 ⬚   8 ⬚   9 ⬚   10 ⬚

I can find the multiplication facts for the 3 times table.

I can recall the multiplication facts for the 3 times table.

Andrew Brodie: Ten Minute Maths Assessments ages 7–8 © A&C Black 2009

Derive and recall multiplication facts for the 4 times table

Building on previous learning

Before starting this unit check that the children can already:
- derive and recall multiplication facts for the 2 times, 5 times and 10 times tables.

Learning objectives

Objective 1: Derive multiplication facts for the 4 times table.

Objective 2: Recall multiplication facts for the 4 times table.

Learning outcomes

The children will be able to:
- derive and recall all multiplication facts for the 4 times table.

Success criteria

The children have a **secure** level of attainment in relation to Objective 1 if the following question can be answered with a 'yes'.

Can the children...
... complete the task on the top half of the Assessment sheet, confidently and independently?

The children have a **secure** level of attainment in relation to Objective 2 if the following question can be answered with a 'yes'.

Can the children...
... respond quickly and accurately to the questions on the CD?

Administering the assessment

🔘 Track 13   Ensure that the children understand the task on the top half of the page. They may need to use the array of squares or counting apparatus to help them. Once they have completed the task of writing out the table, ask them to fold the sheets and to listen carefully to the CD. They should be able to answer the questions without the need to pause the CD. This is the script for the CD if you decide to dictate the questions.

I will say each question twice then you will have five seconds to answer it.
Question 1: What is 4 multiplied by 10?
Question 2: What is 6 times 4?
Question 3: What is the product of 5 and 4?
Question 4: Multiply 4 by 2
Question 5: 8 times 4
Question 6: 4 multiplied by 9
Question 7: What is 4 times 4?
Question 8: 1 times 4
Question 9: What is the product of 3 and 4?
Question 10: What is 7 times 4?

(This assessment will also provide evidence for assessing strand 1, Using and applying mathematics: Identify patterns and relationships involving numbers or shapes.)

Andrew Brodie: Ten Minute Maths Assessments ages 7–8 © A&C Black 2009

Derive and recall multiplication facts for the 4 times table

Name

Date

Write the 4 times table.
It has been started for you.

$1 \times 4 = 4$

$2 \times 4 = 8$

Now fold the paper so that you cannot see the 4 times table.

Listen carefully to the CD or your teacher.

1 ( )   2 ( )   3 ( )   4 ( )   5 ( )

6 ( )   7 ( )   8 ( )   9 ( )   10 ( )

I can find the multiplication facts for the 4 times table.

I can recall the multiplication facts for the 4 times table.

Andrew Brodie: Ten Minute Maths Assessments ages 7–8 © A&C Black 2009

Derive and recall multiplication facts for the 6 times table

Building on previous learning

Before starting this unit check that the children can already:
- derive and recall multiplication facts for the 2 times, 5 times and 10 times tables.

Learning objectives

Objective 1: Derive multiplication facts for the 6 times table.

Objective 2: Recall multiplication facts for the 6 times table.

Learning outcomes

The children will be able to:
- derive and recall all multiplication facts for the 6 times table.

Success criteria

The children have a **secure** level of attainment in relation to Objective 1 if the following question can be answered with a 'yes'.

Can the children...
... complete the task on the top half of the Assessment sheet, confidently and independently?

The children have a **secure** level of attainment in relation to Objective 2 if the following question can be answered with a 'yes'.

Can the children...
... respond quickly and accurately to the questions on the CD?

Administering the assessment

🔘 Track 14 Ensure that the children understand the task on the top half of the page. They may need to use the array of hexagons or counting apparatus to help them. Once they have completed the task of writing out the table, ask them to fold their sheets and listen carefully to the CD. They should be able to answer the questions without the need to pause the CD. This is the script for the CD if you decide to dictate the questions.

I will say each question twice then you will have five seconds to answer it.
Question 1: What is 6 multiplied by 6?
Question 2: What is 9 times 6?
Question 3: What is the product of 2 and 6?
Question 4: Multiply 6 by zero
Question 5: 8 times 6
Question 6: 6 multiplied by 4
Question 7: What is 3 times 6?
Question 8: 5 times 6
Question 9: What is the product of 7 and 6?
Question 10: What is 10 times 6?

(This assessment will also provide evidence for assessing strand 1, Using and applying mathematics: Identify patterns and relationships involving numbers or shapes.)

Derive and recall multiplication facts for the 6 times table

Name

Date

Write the 6 times table.
It has been started for you.

1 x 6 = 6

2 x 6 = 12

Now fold the paper so that you
cannot see the 6 times table.

Listen carefully to the CD or your teacher.

1 ⬭   2 ⬭   3 ⬭   4 ⬭   5 ⬭

6 ⬭   7 ⬭   8 ⬭   9 ⬭   10 ⬭

I can find the multiplication facts for the 6 times table. ⬭

I can recall the multiplication facts for the 6 times table. ⬭

Derive and recall division facts related to the 2 times table

Building on previous learning

Before starting this unit check that the children can already:

- derive and recall multiplication facts for the 2 times table.

Learning objectives

Objective 1: Derive division facts related to the 2 times table

Objective 2: Recall division facts related to the 2 times table.

Objective 3: Understand that division is the inverse of multiplication and vice versa; use this to derive and record related multiplication and division number sentences.

Learning outcomes

The children will be able to:

- derive and recall all division facts for the 2 times table.
- derive and record related multiplication and division number sentences.

Success criteria

The children have a **secure** level of attainment in relation to Objectives 1 and 3 if the following question can be answered with a 'yes'.

Can the children…

… complete the task on the top half of the Assessment sheet, confidently and independently?

The children have a **secure** level of attainment in relation to Objective 2 if the following question can be answered with a 'yes'.

Can the children…

… respond quickly and accurately to the questions on the CD?

Administering the assessment

● Track 15   Ensure that the children understand the task on the top half of the page. They may need to use the array of circles or counting apparatus to help them. Once they have completed the task of writing out the table, ask them to fold their sheets and listen carefully to the CD. They should be able to answer the questions without the need to pause the CD. This is the script for the CD if you decide to dictate the questions.

I will say each question twice then you will have five seconds to answer it.
Question 1: What is 18 divided by 2?
Question 2: What is 12 divided by 2?
Question 3: 20 divided by 2
Question 4: 2 divided by 2
Question 5: 8 divided by 2
Question 6: 4 divided by 2
Question 7: 10 divided by 2
Question 8: 16 divided by 2
Question 9: 6 divided by 2
Question 10: 14 divided by 2

(This assessment will also provide evidence for assessing strand 1, Using and applying mathematics: Identify patterns and relationships involving numbers or shapes.)

Derive and recall division facts related to the 2 times table

Name

Date

Write the 2 times table.
It has been started for you.
Use the 2 times table to write
the division table.

1 x 2 = 2	2 ÷ 2 = 1
2 x 2 = 4	4 ÷ 2 = 2
3 x 2 = 6	6 ÷ 2 = 3

------------------ ------------------

------------------ ------------------

------------------ ------------------

------------------ ------------------

------------------ ------------------

------------------ ------------------

------------------ ------------------

Now fold the paper so
that you cannot see the
2 times table.

Listen carefully to the CD or your teacher.

1 ◻   2 ◻   3 ◻   4 ◻   5 ◻

6 ◻   7 ◻   8 ◻   9 ◻   10 ◻

I can find the division facts related to the 2 times table. ◻

I can recall the division facts related to the 2 times table. ◻

Andrew Brodie: Ten Minute Maths Assessments ages 7–8 © A&C Black 2009

Derive and recall division facts related to the 3 times table

Building on previous learning

Before starting this unit check that the children can already:
- derive and recall multiplication facts for the 3 times table.

Learning objectives

Objective 1: Derive division facts related to the 3 times table.

Objective 2: Recall division facts related to the 3 times table.

Objective 3: Understand that division is the inverse of multiplication and vice versa; use this to derive and record related multiplication and division number sentences.

Learning outcomes

The children will be able to:
- derive and recall all division facts for the 3 times table.
- derive and record related multiplication and division number sentences.

Success criteria

The children have a **secure** level of attainment in relation to Objectives 1 and 3 if the following question can be answered with a 'yes'.

Can the children...
... complete the task on the top half of the Assessment sheet, confidently and independently?

The children have a **secure** level of attainment in relation to Objective 2 if the following question can be answered with a 'yes'.

Can the children...
... respond quickly and accurately to the questions on the CD?

Administering the assessment

🔘 Track 16   Ensure that the children understand the task on the top half of the page. They may need to use the array of triangles or counting apparatus to help them. Once they have completed the task of writing out the table, ask them to fold the sheets and to listen carefully to the CD. They should be able to answer the questions without the need to pause the audio. This is the script for the CD if you decide to dictate the questions.

I will say each question twice then you will have five seconds to answer it.

Question 1: What is 18 divided by 3?
Question 2: What is 12 divided by 3?
Question 3: 6 divided by 3
Question 4: 15 divided by 3
Question 5: 24 divided by 3
Question 6: 3 divided by 3
Question 7: 30 divided by 3
Question 8: 9 divided by 3
Question 9: 27 divided by 3
Question 10: 21 divided by 3

(This assessment will also provide evidence for assessing strand 1, Using and applying mathematics: Identify patterns and relationships involving numbers or shapes.)

Andrew Brodie: Ten Minute Maths Assessments ages 7–8 © A&C Black 2009

Derive and recall division facts related to the 3 times table

Name

Date

Write the 3 times table.
It has been started for you.
Use the 3 times table to write the division table.

1 x 3 = 3	3 ÷ 3 = 1
2 x 3 = 6	6 ÷ 3 = 2

-------------------- --------------------

-------------------- --------------------

-------------------- --------------------

-------------------- --------------------

-------------------- --------------------

-------------------- --------------------

-------------------- --------------------

Now fold the paper so that you cannot see the 3 times table.

Listen carefully to the CD or your teacher.

1 ⬚   2 ⬚   3 ⬚   4 ⬚   5 ⬚

6 ⬚   7 ⬚   8 ⬚   9 ⬚   10 ⬚

I can find the division facts related to the 3 times table.

I can recall the division facts related to the 3 times table.

Derive and recall division facts related to the 4 times table

Building on previous learning

Before starting this unit check that the children can already:
- derive and recall multiplication facts for the 4 times table.

Learning objectives

Objective 1: Derive division facts related to the 4 times table.

Objective 2: Recall division facts related to the 4 times table.

Objective 3: Understand that division is the inverse of multiplication and vice versa; use this to derive and record related multiplication and division number sentences.

Learning outcomes

The children will be able to:
- derive and recall all division facts for the 4 times table.
- derive and record related multiplication and division number sentences.

Success criteria

The children have a **secure** level of attainment in relation to Objectives 1 and 3 if the following question can be answered with a 'yes'.

Can the children…
… complete the task on the top half of the Assessment sheet, confidently and independently?

The children have a **secure** level of attainment in relation to Objective 2 if the following question can be answered with a 'yes'.

Can the children…
… respond quickly and accurately to the questions on the CD?

Administering the assessment

Track 17 Ensure that the children understand the task on the top half of the page. They may need to use the array of squares or counting apparatus to help them. Once they have completed the task of writing out the table, ask them to fold the sheets and to listen carefully to the CD. They should be able to answer the questions without the need to pause the CD. This is the script for the CD if you decide to dictate the questions.

I will say each question twice then you will have five seconds to answer it.
Question 1: What is 36 divided by 4?
Question 2: What is 24 divided by 4?
Question 3: 4 divided by 4
Question 4: 16 divided by 4
Question 5: 32 divided by 4
Question 6: 8 divided by 4
Question 7: 12 divided by 4
Question 8: 20 divided by 4
Question 9: 28 divided by 4
Question 10: 40 divided by 4

(This assessment will also provide evidence for assessing strand 1, Using and applying mathematics: Identify patterns and relationships involving numbers or shapes.)

Andrew Brodie: Ten Minute Maths Assessments ages 7–8 © A&C Black 2009

Derive and recall division facts related to the 4 times table

Name

Date

Write the 4 times table.
It has been started for you.
Use the 4 times table to write
the division table.

$1 \times 4 = 4$ $4 \div 4 = 1$

$2 \times 4 = 8$ $8 \div 4 = 2$

---------------------   ---------------------

---------------------   ---------------------

---------------------   ---------------------

---------------------   ---------------------

---------------------   ---------------------

---------------------   ---------------------

---------------------   ---------------------

Now fold the paper so
that you cannot see the
4 times table.

Listen carefully to the CD or your teacher.

1 [   ]   2 [   ]   3 [   ]   4 [   ]   5 [   ]

6 [   ]   7 [   ]   8 [   ]   9 [   ]   10 [   ]

I can find the division facts related to the 4 times table.

I can recall the division facts related to the 4 times table.

Andrew Brodie: Ten Minute Maths Assessments ages 7–8 © A&C Black 2009

Derive and recall division facts related to the 5 times table

Building on previous learning

Before starting this unit check that the children can already:
- derive and recall multiplication facts for the 5 times table.

Learning objectives

Objective 1: Derive division facts related to the 5 times table.

Objective 2: Recall division facts related to the 5 times table.

Objective 3: Understand that division is the inverse of multiplication and vice versa; use this to derive and record related multiplication and division number sentences.

Learning outcomes

The children will be able to:
- derive and recall all division facts for the 5 times table.
- derive and record related multiplication and division number sentences.

Success criteria

The children have a **secure** level of attainment in relation to Objectives 1 and 3 if the following question can be answered with a 'yes'.

Can the children...
... complete the task on the top half of the Assessment sheet, confidently and independently?

The children have a **secure** level of attainment in relation to Objective 2 if the following question can be answered with a 'yes'.

Can the children...
... respond quickly and accurately to the questions on the CD?

Administering the assessment

● Track 18   Ensure that the children understand the task on the top half of the page. They may need to use the array of pentagons or counting apparatus to help them. Once they have completed the task of writing out the table, ask them to fold the sheets and to listen carefully to the CD. They should be able to answer the questions without the need to pause the CD. This is the script for the CD if you decide to dictate the questions.

I will say each question twice then you will have five seconds to answer it.
Question 1: What is 50 divided by 5?
Question 2: What is 25 divided by 5?
Question 3: 10 divided by 5
Question 4: 45 divided by 5
Question 5: 30 divided by 5
Question 6: 15 divided by 5
Question 7: 5 divided by 5
Question 8: 20 divided by 5
Question 9: 40 divided by 5
Question 10: 35 divided by 5

(This assessment will also provide evidence for assessing strand 1, Using and applying mathematics: Identify patterns and relationships involving numbers or shapes.)

Derive and recall division facts related to the 5 times table

Name

Date

Write the 5 times table.
It has been started for you.
Use the 5 times table to write
the division table.

1 x 5 = 5   5 ÷ 5 = 1

2 x 5 = 10   10 ÷ 5 = 2

-------------------   -------------------

-------------------   -------------------

-------------------   -------------------

-------------------   -------------------

-------------------   -------------------

Now fold the paper so
that you cannot see the
5 times table.

-------------------   -------------------

-------------------   -------------------

Listen carefully to the CD or your teacher.

1 ⬜   2 ⬜   3 ⬜   4 ⬜   5 ⬜

6 ⬜   7 ⬜   8 ⬜   9 ⬜   10 ⬜

I can find the division facts related to the 5 times table.   ⬜

I can recall the division facts related to the 5 times table.   ⬜

Derive and recall division facts related to the 6 times table

Building on previous learning

Before starting this unit check that the children can already:
- derive and recall multiplication facts for the 6 times table.

Learning objectives

Objective 1: Derive division facts related to the 6 times table.

Objective 2: Recall division facts related to the 6 times table.

Objective 3: Understand that division is the inverse of multiplication and vice versa; use this to derive and record related multiplication and division number sentences.

Learning outcomes

The children will be able to:
- derive and recall all division facts for the 6 times table.
- derive and record related multiplication and division number sentences.

Success criteria

The children have a **secure** level of attainment in relation to Objectives 1 and 3 if the following question can be answered with a 'yes'.

Can the children…
… complete the task on the top half of the Assessment sheet, confidently and independently?

The children have a **secure** level of attainment in relation to Objective 2 if the following question can be answered with a 'yes'.

Can the children…
… respond quickly and accurately to the questions on the CD?

Administering the assessment

Track 19 Ensure that the children understand the task on the top half of the page. They may need to use the array of hexagons or counting apparatus to help them. Once they have completed the task of writing out the table, ask them to fold the sheets then to listen carefully to the CD. They should be able to answer the questions without the need to pause the CD. This is the script for the CD if you decide to dictate the questions.

I will say each question twice then you will have five seconds to answer it.
Question 1: What is 6 divided by 6?
Question 2: What is 30 divided by 6?
Question 3: 60 divided by 6
Question 4: 12 divided by 6
Question 5: 36 divided by 6
Question 6: 18 divided by 6
Question 7: 24 divided by 6
Question 8: 42 divided by 6
Question 9: 54 divided by 6
Question 10: 48 divided by 6

(This assessment will also provide evidence for assessing strand 1, Using and applying mathematics: Identify patterns and relationships involving numbers or shapes.)

Derive and recall division facts related to the 6 times table

Name

Date

Write the 6 times table.
It has been started for you.
Use the 6 times table to write the division table.

$1 \times 6 = 6$ $6 \div 6 = 1$

$2 \times 6 = 12$ $12 \div 6 = 2$

-------------------   -------------------

-------------------   -------------------

-------------------   -------------------

-------------------   -------------------

-------------------   -------------------

-------------------   -------------------

-------------------   -------------------

Now fold the paper so that you cannot see the 6 times table.

Listen carefully to the CD or your teacher.

1 ▢   2 ▢   3 ▢   4 ▢   5 ▢

6 ▢   7 ▢   8 ▢   9 ▢   10 ▢

I can find the division facts related to the 6 times table.   ▢

I can recall the division facts related to the 6 times table.   ▢

Derive and recall division facts related to the 10 times table

Building on previous learning

Before starting this unit check that the children can already:

- derive and recall multiplication facts for the 10 times table.

Learning objectives

Objective 1: Derive division facts related to the 10 times table.

Objective 2: Recall division facts related to the 10 times table.

Objective 3: Understand that division is the inverse of multiplication and vice versa; use this to derive and record related multiplication and division number sentences.

Learning outcomes

The children will be able to:

- derive and recall all division facts for the 10 times table.
- derive and record related multiplication and division number sentences.

Success criteria

The children have a **secure** level of attainment in relation to Objectives 1 and 3 if the following question can be answered with a 'yes'.

Can the children…
… complete the task on the top half of the Assessment sheet, confidently and independently?

The children have a **secure** level of attainment in relation to Objective 2 if the following question can be answered with a 'yes'.

Can the children…
… respond quickly and accurately to the questions on the CD?

Administering the assessment

⬤ Track 20   Ensure that the children understand the task on the top half of the page. They may need to use the array of squares or counting apparatus to help them. Once they have completed the task of writing out the table, ask them to fold the sheets and to listen carefully to the CD. They should be able to answer the questions without the need to pause the CD. This is the script for the CD if you decide to dictate the questions.

I will say each question twice then you will have five seconds to answer it.
Question 1: What is 40 divided by 10?
Question 2: What is 10 divided by 10?
Question 3: 60 divided by 10
Question 4: 90 divided by 10
Question 5: 100 divided by 10
Question 6: 50 divided by 10
Question 7: 20 divided by 10
Question 8: 70 divided by 10
Question 9: 30 divided by 10
Question 10: 80 divided by 10

(This assessment will also provide evidence for assessing strand 1, Using and applying mathematics: Identify patterns and relationships involving numbers or shapes.)

Andrew Brodie: Ten Minute Maths Assessments ages 7–8 © A&C Black 2009

Derive and recall division facts related to the 10 times table

Name

Date

Write the 10 times table.
It has been started for you.
Use the 10 times table to write
the division table.

| $1 \times 10 = 10$ | $10 \div 10 = 1$ |
| $2 \times 10 = 20$ | $20 \div 10 = 2$ |

----------------------   ----------------------

----------------------   ----------------------

----------------------   ----------------------

----------------------   ----------------------

----------------------   ----------------------

----------------------   ----------------------

----------------------   ----------------------

Now fold the paper so
that you cannot see the
10 times table.

Listen carefully to the CD or your teacher.

1 ☐   2 ☐   3 ☐   4 ☐   5 ☐

6 ☐   7 ☐   8 ☐   9 ☐   10 ☐

I can find the division facts related to the 10 times table. ☐

I can recall the division facts related to the 10 times table. ☐

Andrew Brodie: Ten Minute Maths Assessments ages 7–8 © A&C Black 2009

Recognise multiples of 2, 5 or 10 up to 1000

Building on previous learning

Before starting this unit check that the children can already:
- count on or back in ones, twos, fives and tens and use this knowledge to derive the multiples of 2, 5 and 10 to the tenth multiple.
- describe and extend number sequences.
- recognise odd and even numbers.

Learning objectives

Objective 1: Recognise multiples of 2 up to 1000.
Objective 2: Recognise multiples of 5 up to 1000.
Objective 2: Recognise multiples of 10 up to 1000.

Learning outcomes

The children will be able to:
- recognise that multiples of 2 always have 0, 2, 4, 6 or 8 as the units (ones) value.
- recognise that multiples of 5 always have 0 or 5 as the units (ones) value.
- recognise that multiples of 10 always have 0 as the units (ones) value.

Success criteria

The children have a **secure** level of attainment in relation to Objective 1 if the following questions can be answered with a 'yes'.

Can the children…
… continue each of the sequences shown on the Assessment sheet confidently and quickly?
… answer the six questions about multiples confidently and quickly?
… explain why a number is or is not a multiple of 2, 5 or 10?

Administering the assessment

Ensure that the children understand the sequencing tasks. Discuss each sequence with them to assess whether they can identify the emerging patterns. Have they noticed that multiples of 2 always have 0, 2, 4, 6 or 8 as the units (ones) value? You may decide to ask further questions of the type shown on the bottom half of the Assessment sheet.

(This assessment will also provide evidence for assessing strand 1, Using and applying mathematics: Identify patterns and relationships involving numbers or shapes; Describe and explain methods choices and solutions to puzzles and problems, orally and in writing.)

Andrew Brodie: Ten Minute Maths Assessments ages 7–8 © A&C Black 2009

Recognise multiples of 2, 5 or 10 up to 1000

Name _____ **Date** _____

Continue this sequence of multiples of 2: 2, 4, 6, 8, 10,

◯ , ◯ , ◯ , ◯ , ◯ , ◯ , ◯ , ◯ , ◯ , ◯ ...

Continue this sequence of multiples of 5: 5, 10, 15, 20, 25,

◯ , ◯ , ◯ , ◯ , ◯ , ◯ , ◯ , ◯ , ◯ , ◯ ...

Continue this sequence of multiples of 10: 10, 20, 30, 40, 50,

◯ , ◯ , ◯ , ◯ , ◯ , ◯ , ◯ , ◯ , ◯ , ◯ ...

Continue this sequence of multiples of 2: 250, 252, 254, 256, 258,

◯ , ◯ , ◯ , ◯ , ◯ ...

Continue this sequence of multiples of 5: 675, 680, 685, 690, 695,

◯ , ◯ , ◯ , ◯ , ◯ ...

Continue this sequence of multiples of 10: 750, 760, 770, 780, 790,

◯ , ◯ , ◯ , ◯ , ◯ ...

Answer yes or no to these questions:

Is 573 a multiple of 2? ◯   Is 698 a multiple of 2? ◯

Is 695 a multiple of 5? ◯   Is 740 a multiple of 5? ◯

Is 1000 a multiple of 10? ◯   Is 999 a multiple of 10? ◯

I can recognise multiples of 2, 5 or 10 up to 1000. ✏️◯

Andrew Brodie: Ten Minute Maths Assessments ages 7–8 © A&C Black 2009

Add mentally combinations of one-digit and two-digit numbers

Building on previous learning

Before starting this unit check that the children can already:
- derive and recall all addition facts for each number to 20.
- derive and recall sums and differences of multiples of 10.
- derive and recall number pairs that total 100.

Learning objectives

Objective 1: Add mentally combinations of one-digit and two-digit numbers.

Learning outcomes

The children will be able to:
- add mentally combinations of one-digit and two-digit numbers.

Success criteria

The children have a **secure** level of attainment in relation to Objective 1 if the following question can be answered with a 'yes'.

Can the children…
… complete the assessment questions confidently and quickly?

Administering the assessment

Track 21 Ensure that the children understand how they are to show their answers on the Assessment sheet. The pupils are being assessed on their ability to add 'mentally' and therefore the only written work required is the answer to each question. However, they should be allowed to make simple jottings, to refer to a number line or to use their fingers if necessary. The assessment should reflect how confidently and quickly they can complete the questions. The CD is used for this assessment. Note that the final five questions are in the context of money. This is the script for the CD if you decide to dictate the questions.

I will say each question twice then you will have ten seconds to answer it.
Question 1: 15 add 7
Question 2: 32 plus 8
Question 3: 47 add 5
Question 4: 69 plus 9
Question 5: 8 add 27
Question 6: 4 plus 88
Question 7: 5 add 75
Question 8: 9 plus 94
Question 9: 12 add 8
Question 10: 28 plus 9
Question 11: 67 add 7
Question 12: What is the total of 69p and 8p?
Question 13: I have 45p and 5p. How much do I have altogether?
Question 14: How much is 2p plus 58p?
Question 15: What is the total value of 7p and 85p?
Question 16: I have 8p and 92p. What is the total amount?

(This assessment will also provide evidence for assessing strand 1, Using and applying mathematics: Solve one-step problems involving numbers, money or measures; Identify patterns and relationships involving numbers or shapes.)

Add mentally combinations of one-digit and two-digit numbers

Name

Date

Listen carefully to the CD or your teacher. Write your answers in the correct boxes.

1. ( ) 15, 7

2. ( ) 32, 8

3. ( ) 47, 5

4. ( ) 69, 9

5. ( ) 8, 27

6. ( ) 4, 88

7. ( ) 5, 75

8. ( ) 9, 94

9. ( ) 12, 8

10. ( ) 28, 9

11. ( ) 67, 7

12. ( ) 69p, 8p

13. ( ) 45p, 5p

14. ( ) 58p, 2p

15. ( ) 7p, 85p

16. ( ) 8p, 92p

I can add mentally combinations of one-digit and two-digit numbers.

Andrew Brodie: Ten Minute Maths Assessments ages 7–8 © A&C Black 2009

Subtract mentally combinations of one-digit and two-digit numbers

Building on previous learning

Before starting this unit check that the children can already:
- derive and recall all subtraction facts for each number to 20.
- derive and recall sums and differences of multiples of 10.
- derive and recall number pairs that total 100.

Learning objectives

Objective 1: Subtract mentally combinations of one-digit and two-digit numbers.

Learning outcomes

The children will be able to:
- subtract mentally combinations of one-digit and two-digit numbers.

Success criteria

The children have a **secure** level of attainment in relation to Objective 1 if the following question can be answered with a 'yes'.

Can the children...
... complete the assessment questions confidently and quickly?

Administering the assessment

🔘 Track 22 Ensure that the children understand how they are to show their answers on the Assessment sheet. The pupils are being assessed on their ability to subtract 'mentally' and therefore the only written work required is the answer to each question. However, they should be allowed to make simple jottings, to refer to a number line or to use their fingers if necessary. The assessment should reflect how confidently and quickly they can complete the questions. The CD is used for this assessment. Note that the final five questions are in the context of money. This is the script for the CD if you decide to dictate the questions.

I will say each question twice then you will have ten seconds to answer it.
Question 1: 25 subtract 4
Question 2: 49 minus 8
Question 3: 85 take away 3
Question 4: 99 take 6
Question 5: 43 subtract 7
Question 6: 67 take 9
Question 7: 72 take away 8
Question 8: 81 subtract 5
Question 9: 33 minus 9
Question 10: 51 take 2
Question 11: 83 minus 6
Question 12: I have 50p and spend 8p. How much do I have left?
Question 13: I have 62p and spend 9p. How much do I have left?
Question 14: I have 40p and spend 1p. How much do I have left?
Question 15: I have 34p and spend 9p. How much do I have left?
Question 16: I have 78p and spend 6p. How much do I have left?

(This assessment will also provide evidence for assessing strand 1, Using and applying mathematics: Solve one-step problems involving numbers, money or measures; Identify patterns and relationships involving numbers or shapes.)

Subtract mentally combinations of one-digit and two-digit numbers

Name

Date

Listen carefully to the CD or your teacher. Write your answers in the correct boxes.

1. ⬭ 25, 4

2. ⬭ 49, 8

3. ⬭ 85, 3

4. ⬭ 99, 6

5. ⬭ 43, 7

6. ⬭ 67, 9

7. ⬭ 72, 8

8. ⬭ 81, 5

9. ⬭ 33, 9

10. ⬭ 51, 2

11. ⬭ 83, 6

12. ⬭ 50p, 8p

13. ⬭ 62p, 9p

14. ⬭ 40p, 1p

15. ⬭ 34p, 9p

16. ⬭ 78p, 6p

I can subtract mentally combinations of one-digit and two-digit numbers. ⬭

Develop and use written methods to record, support or explain addition of two-digit and three-digit numbers

Building on previous learning

Before starting this unit check that the children can already:

- derive and recall all addition facts for each number to 20.
- derive and recall sums and differences of multiples of 10.
- derive and recall number pairs that total 100.

Learning objectives

Objective 1: Develop and use written methods to record, support or explain addition of two-digit and three-digit numbers.

Learning outcomes

The children will be able to:

- use their own strategies to add two-digit numbers to three-digit numbers.

Success criteria

The children have a **secure** level of attainment in relation to Objective 1 if the following question can be answered with a 'yes'.

Can the children…

… complete the assessment questions confidently and quickly by using an appropriate strategy for addition?

Administering the assessment

Discuss the layout of the Assessment sheet with the pupils, pointing out that space is provided for working out the answers to the questions. The assessment concerns whether the pupils have an appropriate written strategy for addition of two-digit and three-digit numbers. Each child's strategy may be a method that they have been shown in school or at home but it could also be a method of their own devising, perhaps using numbers, pictures or diagrams. You may need to refer to your school policy on calculation, which will specify an appropriate method.

The final question is an extension activity as it puts the operation in the context of problem solving. Some children will need help with reading the question.

(This assessment will also provide evidence for assessing strand 1, Using and applying mathematics: Solve one-step problems involving numbers, money or measures; Represent the information in a puzzle or problem using numbers, images or diagrams; Identify patterns and relationships involving numbers or shapes; Describe and explain methods, choices and solutions to puzzles and problems, orally and in writing, using pictures and diagrams.)

Develop and use written methods to support addition of two-digit and three-digit numbers

Name

Date

Look carefully at each addition question.
Use the space to show your working out.

256 + 38

Answer

429 + 53

Answer

198 + 67

Answer

Beth has saved £146. Sam gives her £52.
How much has she got now?

Answer

I can use written methods for the addition of two-digit and three-digit numbers.

Develop and use written methods to record, support or explain subtraction of two-digit and three-digit numbers

Building on previous learning

Before starting this unit check that the children can already:

- derive and recall all subtraction facts for each number to 20.
- derive and recall sums and differences of multiples of 10.
- derive and recall number pairs that total 100.

Learning objectives

Objective 1: Develop and use written methods to record, support or explain subtraction of two-digit and three-digit numbers.

Learning outcomes

The children will be able to:

- use their own strategies to subtract two-digit numbers from three-digit numbers.

Success criteria

The children have a **secure** level of attainment in relation to Objective 1 if the following question can be answered with a 'yes'.

Can the children…

… complete the assessment questions confidently and quickly by using an appropriate strategy for subtraction?

Administering the assessment

Discuss the layout of the Assessment sheet with the pupils, pointing out that space is provided for working out the answers to the questions. The assessment focuses on whether the pupils have an appropriate written strategy for subtraction of two-digit and three-digit numbers. Each child's strategy may be a method that they have been shown in school or at home but it could also be a method of their own devising, perhaps using numbers, pictures or diagrams. You may need to refer to your school policy on calculation, which will specify an appropriate method. The final question is an extension activity as it puts the operation in the context of problem solving. Some children will need help with reading the question.

(This assessment will also provide evidence for assessing strand 1, Using and applying mathematics: Solve one-step problems involving numbers, money or measures; Represent the information in a puzzle or problem using numbers, images or diagrams; Identify patterns and relationships involving numbers or shapes; Describe and explain methods, choices and solutions to puzzles and problems, orally and in writing, using pictures and diagrams.)

Develop and use written methods to support subtraction of two-digit and three-digit numbers

Name

Date

Look carefully at each subtraction question.
Use the space to show your working out.

500 – 69

Answer

147 – 32

Answer

348 – 86

Answer

Dave is walking around a 400 metre track.
He has walked 75 metres. How much further does he need to walk?

Answer

I can use written methods for the subtraction of two-digit and three-digit numbers

Andrew Brodie: Ten Minute Maths Assessments ages 7–8 © A&C Black 2009

Multiply one-digit and two-digit numbers by 10 or 100 and describe the effect

Building on previous learning

Before starting this unit check that the children can already:
- recognise multiples of 10 up to 1000.
- recall multiplication facts for the 10 times table.

Learning objectives

Objective 1: Multiply one-digit or two-digit numbers by 10 and describe the effect.
Objective 2: Multiply one-digit or two-digit numbers by 100 and describe the effect.

Learning outcomes

The children will be able to:
- multiply one-digit and two-digit numbers by 10 or 100.
- describe the mathematical effect of multiplying by 10 or 100.

Success criteria

The children have a **secure** level of attainment in relation to Objective 1 if the following question can be answered with a 'yes'.

Can the children…
… complete the assessment questions confidently and quickly?

Administering the assessment

🔘 Track 23   Before starting the written part of the assessment discuss some questions with the children e.g. 35 x 10 and 4 x 100. Can each child explain what is happening? Don't accept 'adding a zero' or 'adding two zeroes' – this is not what is happening! Instead the children should be able to explain the process in relation to place value. Ensure that the children understand how they are to show their answers on the Assessment sheet. Ask the children to listen carefully to the CD. They should be able to answer the questions very quickly without the need to pause it. This is the script for the CD if you decide to dictate the questions.

I will say each question twice then you will have five seconds to answer it.
Question 1: 10 times 7
Question 2: 49 times 10
Question 3: 100 times 6
Question 4: 10 times 54
Question 5: 4 times 100
Question 6: 93 times 10
Question 7: 48 times 10
Question 8: 3 times 10
Question 9: 3 times 100
Question 10: 52 times 100
Question 11: 100 times 9
Question 12: 84 times 100
Question 13: 10 times 81
Question 14: 100 times 99
Question 15: 35 times 100
Question 16: 10 times 45

(This assessment will also provide evidence for assessing strand 1, Using and applying mathematics: Identify patterns and relationships involving numbers or shapes.)

Andrew Brodie: Ten Minute Maths Assessments ages 7–8 © A&C Black 2009

Multiply one-digit and two-digit numbers by 10 or 100 and describe the effect

Name

Date

Listen carefully to the CD or your teacher. Write your answers in the correct boxes.

1. ( ) 7

2. ( ) 49

3. ( ) 6

4. ( ) 54

5. ( ) 4

6. ( ) 93

7. ( ) 48

8. ( ) 3

9. ( ) 3

10. ( ) 52

11. ( ) 9

12. ( ) 84

13. ( ) 81

14. ( ) 99

15. ( ) 35

16. ( ) 45

I can multiply one-digit and two-digit numbers by 10 or 100.

Andrew Brodie: Ten Minute Maths Assessments ages 7–8 © A&C Black 2009

Use practical and informal written methods to multiply two-digit numbers by one-digit numbers

Building on previous learning

Before starting this unit check that the children can already:

- derive and recall multiplication facts for the 2, 3, 4, 5, 6 and 10 times-tables.

Learning objectives

Objective 1: Use practical and informal written methods to multiply two-digit numbers by one-digit numbers.

Learning outcomes

The children will be able to:

- use their own strategies to multiply two-digit numbers by one-digit numbers.

Success criteria

The children have a **secure** level of attainment in relation to Objective 1 if the following question can be answered with a 'yes'.

Can the children…

… complete the assessment questions confidently and quickly by using an appropriate strategy for multiplication?

Administering the assessment

Discuss the layout of the Assessment sheet with the pupils, pointing out that space is provided for working out the answers to the questions. The assessment focuses on whether the pupils have an appropriate practical or written strategy for multiplication of two-digit numbers by one-digit numbers. Each child's strategy may be a method that they have been shown in school or at home but it could also be a method of their own devising, perhaps using numbers, pictures, diagrams or equipment. You may need to refer to your school policy on calculation, which will specify an appropriate method. The final question is an extension activity as it puts the operation in the context of a problem. Some children will need help with reading the question.

(This assessment will also provide evidence for assessing strand 1, Using and applying mathematics: Solve one-step problems involving numbers, money or measures; Represent the information in a puzzle or problem using numbers, images or diagrams; Identify patterns and relationships involving numbers or shapes; Describe and explain methods, choices and solutions to puzzles and problems, orally and in writing, using pictures and diagrams.)

Use practical and informal written methods to multiply two-digit numbers by one-digit numbers

Name

Date

Look carefully at each multiplication question.
Use the space to show your working out.

15 x 3

Answer

16 x 4

Answer

23 x 2

Answer

One book has 32 pages.
How many pages in total do four of these books have?

Answer

I can multiply two-digit numbers by one-digit numbers.

Use practical and informal written methods to divide two-digit by one-digit numbers

Building on previous learning

Before starting this unit check that the children can already:

- derive and recall multiplication facts for the 2, 3, 4, 5, 6 and 10 times-tables.

Learning objectives

Objective 1: Use practical and informal written methods to divide two-digit numbers by one-digit numbers.

Learning outcomes

The children will be able to:

- use their own strategies to divide two-digit numbers by one-digit numbers.

Success criteria

The children have a **secure** level of attainment in relation to Objective 1 if the following question can be answered with a 'yes'.

Can the children…

… complete the assessment questions confidently and quickly by using an appropriate strategy for division?

Administering the assessment

Discuss the layout of the Assessment sheet with the pupils, pointing out that space is provided for working out the answers to the questions. The assessment focuses on whether the pupils have an appropriate practical or written strategy for division of two-digit numbers by one-digit numbers. Each child's strategy may be a method that they have been shown in school or at home but it could also be a method of their own devising, perhaps using numbers, pictures, diagrams or equipment. You may need to refer to your school policy on calculation, which will specify an appropriate method. The fourth question on the Assessment sheet involves a remainder. If the child is confident with division s/he will be able to produce an appropriate answer.

(This assessment will also provide evidence for assessing strand 1, Using and applying mathematics: Solve one-step problems involving numbers, money or measures; Represent the information in a puzzle or problem using numbers, images or diagrams; Identify patterns and relationships involving numbers or shapes; Describe and explain methods, choices and solutions to puzzles and problems, orally and in writing, using pictures and diagrams.)

Use practical and informal written methods to divide two-digit by one-digit numbers

Name

Date

Look carefully at each division question.
Use the space to show your working out.

20 ÷ 4

Answer

36 ÷ 9

Answer

48 ÷ 3

Answer

50 ÷ 4

Answer

I can divide two-digit numbers by one-digit numbers.

Find unit fractions of numbers and quantities

Building on previous learning

Before starting this unit check that the children can already:
- derive and recall multiplication and division facts for the 2, 3, 4, 5, 6 and 10 times-tables.
- read and write proper fractions.

Learning objectives

Objective 1: Find unit fractions of numbers and quantities.

Learning outcomes

The children will be able to:
- find unit fractions of numbers and quantities.

Success criteria

The children have a **secure** level of attainment in relation to Objective 1 if the following question can be answered with a 'yes'.

Can the children…

… complete the assessment question confidently and quickly?

Administering the assessment

● Track 24   Ensure that the children understand how to show their answers on the Assessment sheet. Encourage them to count the number of fish before the test starts. Allow the use of colouring pens or crayons. This is the script for the CD if you decide to dictate the questions.

I will say each question twice then you will have ten seconds to answer it.
Question 1: One third of all the fish are red. How many are red?
Question 2: Half of all the fish are yellow. How many are yellow?
Question 3: One sixth of all the fish are green. How many are green?
Question 4: The path is 12 metres long. What is one half of 12 metres?
Question 5: The path is 12 metres long. What is one quarter of 12 metres?
Question 6: The path is 12 metres long. What is one third of 12 metres?
Question 7: The path is 12 metres long. What is one sixth of 12 metres?
Question 8: What is one half of 20?
Question 9: What is one quarter of 20?
Question 10: What is one fifth of 20?
Question 11: What is one third of 6?
Question 12: What is one sixth of 18?

(This assessment will also provide evidence for assessing strand 1, Using and applying mathematics: Solve one-step problems involving numbers, money or measures; Represent the information in a puzzle or problem using numbers, images or diagrams; Identify patterns and relationships involving numbers or shapes; Describe and explain methods, choices and solutions to puzzles and problems, orally and in writing, using pictures and diagrams.)

Andrew Brodie: Ten Minute Maths Assessments ages 7–8 © A&C Black 2009

Find unit fractions of numbers and quantities

Name

Date

Listen carefully to the CD or your teacher.

1 ⬭ **2** ⬭ **3** ⬭

4 ⬭ **5** ⬭ **6** ⬭ **7** ⬭

8 ⬭ **9** ⬭ **10** ⬭ **11** ⬭ **12** ⬭

I can find unit fractions of numbers and quantities.

Andrew Brodie: Ten Minute Maths Assessments ages 7–8 © A&C Black 2009

Describe, visualise, classify and draw 2-D shapes

Building on previous learning

Before starting this unit check that the children can already:

- visualise and name common 2-D shapes and describe their features.
- sort, make and describe shapes, referring to their properties.

Learning objectives

Objective 1: Describe, visualise, classify and draw 2-D shapes.

Learning outcomes

The children will be able to:

- describe mathematically and draw, with some degree of accuracy, 2-D shapes.

Success criteria

The children have a **secure** level of attainment in relation to Objective 1 if the following questions can be answered with a 'yes'.

Can the children...

... draw the shapes indicated on the Assessment sheet?
... describe the properties of the shapes using terms such as straight, side, and corner?

Administering the assessment

Ensure that the children can read the words on the Assessment sheet. Use the opportunity to discuss each shape. Can the children describe each one referring to properties such as number of sides and number of corners? Can they distinguish between the square and the rectangle? Can they explain that the square has four equal sides and that its corners are right angles? Can they explain that the opposite sides of the rectangle are equal and that its corners are right angles?

Encourage the children to use rulers for drawing straight sides. Note that the square and the rectangle should have right angles for the corners and should have sides of appropriate length. The other shapes do not have to be regular but, of course, the triangle should have 3 straight sides, the pentagon 5 straight sides, the hexagon 6 straight sides and the octagon 8 straight sides. You may decide to use this assessment to assess another requirement specified in the framework: Use a set-square to draw right angles and to identify right angles in 2-D shapes.

(This assessment will also provide evidence for assessing strand 1, Using and applying mathematics: Identify patterns and relationships involving numbers or shapes; Describe and explain methods, choices and solutions to puzzles and problems, orally and in writing, using pictures and diagrams.)

Andrew Brodie: Ten Minute Maths Assessments ages 7–8 © A&C Black 2009

Describe, visualise, classify and draw 2-D shapes

Name

Date

Draw the correct shape in each box.

square	triangle

rectangle	pentagon

hexagon	octagon

I can describe, visualise, classify and draw 2-D shapes.

Draw and complete shapes with reflective symmetry (draw the reflection of a shape in a mirror line along one side)

Building on previous learning

Before starting this unit check that the children can already:
- visualise and name common 2-D shapes and describe their features.
- sort, make and describe shapes, referring to their properties.
- identify reflective symmetry in patterns.
- identify reflective symmetry in 2-D shapes and draw lines of symmetry in shapes.

Learning objectives

Objective 1: Draw and complete shapes with reflective symmetry; draw the reflection of a shape in a mirror line along one side.

Learning outcomes

The children will be able to:
- draw the reflections of shapes in a mirror line, creating completed shapes with reflected symmetry.

Success criteria

The children have a **secure** level of attainment in relation to Objective 1 if the following question can be answered with a 'yes'.

Can the children...
... draw the reflections of the shapes indicated on the Assessment sheet to produce shapes with reflective symmetry?

Administering the assessment

Ensure that the children understand the assessment task, by helping them to complete the first symmetrical shape. It would be helpful if you could have mirrors available to enable the children to test their pictures. Encourage them to tell you where they think they will need to shade before they actually do so.

(This assessment will also provide evidence for assessing strand 1, Using and applying mathematics: Identify patterns and relationships involving numbers or shapes; Describe and explain methods, choices and solutions to puzzles and problems, orally and in writing, using pictures and diagrams.)

Andrew Brodie: Ten Minute Maths Assessments ages 7–8 © A&C Black 2009

Draw and complete shapes with reflective symmetry

Name

Date

Draw the reflection of each of the shapes using the mirror lines shown.

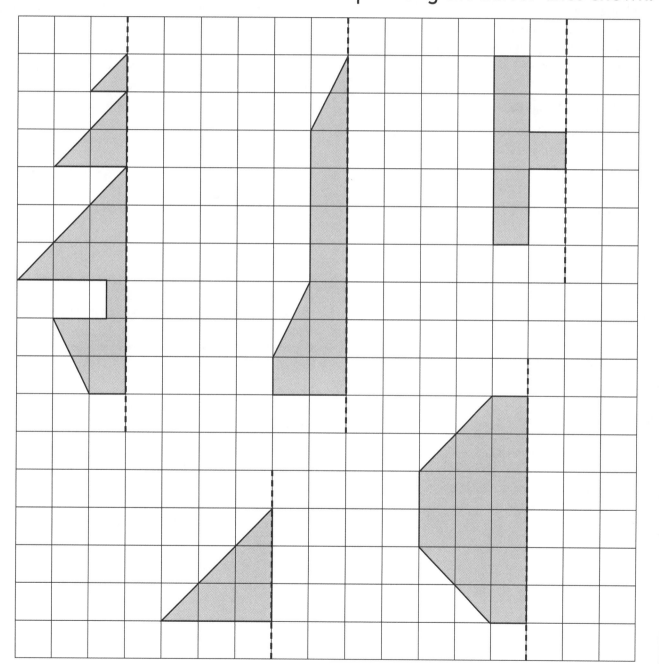

I can draw and complete shapes with reflective symmetry.

I can draw the reflection of a shape in a mirror line along one side.

Andrew Brodie: Ten Minute Maths Assessments ages 7–8 © A&C Black 2009

Read and record the vocabulary of position, direction and movement, using the four compass directions to describe movement about a grid

Building on previous learning

Before starting this unit check that the children can already:
- follow and give instructions involving position, direction and movement.
- recognise and use whole, half and quarter turns, both clockwise and anticlockwise; know that a right angle represents a quarter turn.

Learning objectives

Objective 1: Read and record the vocabulary of position, direction and movement, using the four compass directions to describe movement about a grid.

Learning outcomes

The children will be able to:
- follow the four compass directions to move about a grid.
- use the four compass directions to describe movement about a grid.

Success criteria

The children have a **secure** level of attainment in relation to Objective 1 if the following questions can be answered with a 'yes'.

Can the children…
- … follow the instructions to plot the movement of the hot-air balloon on the grid provided on the Assessment sheet?
- … give instructions to move an object about a grid using the four compass directions?

Administering the assessment

🔘 **Track 25** Ensure that the children can read the instructions on the Assessment sheet. Play the CD, pausing after the first instruction to check that the children understand what to do. This is the script for the CD if you decide to dictate the instructions.

Look at the grid. Look where the hot-air balloon is. Follow the instructions carefully. Instruction 1: The hot-air balloon moves five squares east. Draw a line to show this.
Instruction 2: The hot-air balloon moves four squares north. Draw the route.
Instruction 3: The hot-air balloon moves three squares west. Draw the route.
Instruction 4: The hot-air balloon moves four squares north. Draw the route.
Instruction 5: The hot-air balloon moves six squares east. Draw the route.
Instruction 6: The hot-air balloon moves five squares south. Draw the route.
Instruction 7: The hot-air balloon moves two squares east. Draw the route.
Instruction 8: The hot-air balloon moves eight squares north. Draw the route.
Instruction 9: The hot-air balloon moves one square east, then stops. Colour the square.

Now ask the pupils to give instructions to move an object about the grid. If you prefer you could photocopy page 96, which features a blank grid.

(This assessment will also provide evidence for assessing strand 1, Using and applying mathematics: Represent the information in a puzzle or problem using numbers, images or diagrams; Describe and explain methods, choices and solutions to puzzles and problems, orally and in writing, using pictures and diagrams.)

Read and record the vocabulary of position, direction and movement

Name

Date

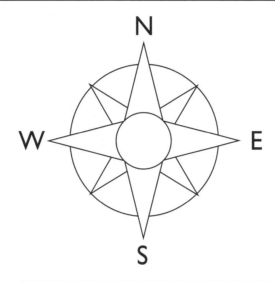

Listen to the instructions and draw the route of the hot-air balloon.

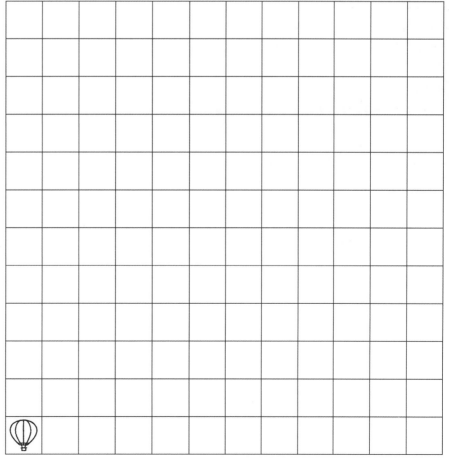

I can use the four compass directions to describe movement about a grid.

Compare angles with a right angle

Building on previous learning

Before starting this unit check that the children can already:

- use a set-square to draw right angles.
- identify right angles in 2-D shapes.

Learning objectives

Objective 1: Compare angles with a right angle.
Objective 2: Make and use lists and tables to organise and interpret information.

Learning outcomes

The children will be able to:

- compare angles with a right angle and sort them into classifications of 'right angle', 'bigger than a right angle', and 'smaller than a right angle'.

Success criteria

The children have a **secure** level of attainment in relation to Objective 1 if the following questions can be answered with a 'yes'.

Can the children…
… compare the angles on the Assessment sheet to a right angle, using equipment such as a set square or folded paper to help them?
… sort the angles into lists and into a table?

Administering the assessment

Ensure that the children can read the instructions on the Assessment sheet. Encourage them to sort the angles according to whether they are right angles or bigger or smaller than right angles. They could use set-squares, or they could use any piece of paper folded carefully twice to make a right angle, to place against each angle.

(This assessment will provide evidence for assessing strand 1, Using and applying mathematics: Make and use lists and tables to organise and interpret information; Identify patterns and relationships involving numbers or shapes; Describe and explain methods, choices and solutions to puzzles and problems, orally and in writing, using pictures and diagrams.)

Andrew Brodie: Ten Minute Maths Assessments ages 7–8 © A&C Black 2009

Compare angles with a right angle

Name

Date

89

Look at each angle. Decide whether it is a right angle, bigger than a right angle or smaller than a right angle.

Cut out the angles and sort them.
Make a table showing right angle, bigger than a right angle, smaller than a right angle.

I can identify right angles and compare other angles to them.

Read the time to the nearest 5 minutes on an analogue clock

Building on previous learning

Before starting this unit check that the children can already:

- read time to the hour, half hour and quarter hour.

Learning objectives

Objective 1: Read the time to the nearest 5 minutes on an analogue clock.

Learning outcomes

The children will be able to:

- read and write down times to the 5 minutes shown on analogue clocks.

Success criteria

The children have a **secure** level of attainment in relation to Objective 1 if the following questions can be answered with a 'yes'.

Can the children...

... write the times shown on the clocks on the Assessment sheet?

... tell the time to the nearest five minutes on hand-held classroom clocks?

Administering the assessment

The Assessment sheet can be used to provide written evidence of attainment. Pupils should be allowed to record the times using numbers and words e.g. 25 past 11, quarter to 12, etc. This activity provides the opportunity to remind the pupils of the pattern of the 5 times table and of the multiples of 5 to 60. The second part of the assessment activity should be completed orally using a hand-held geared classroom clock. Here the assessment is based on whether the children can identify times that are close to the 5 minute intervals e.g. the children should be able to read the time as 'about 5 past 5' on a clock showing a time of '7 minutes past 5'.

You may decide to extend the activity, to cover the requirement for pupils to read the time on a 12-hour digital clock, by asking the children to match digital clock times to those shown on the analogue clock.

(This assessment will provide evidence for assessing strand 1, Using and applying mathematics: Identify patterns and relationships involving numbers or shapes; Describe and explain methods, choices and solutions to puzzles and problems, orally and in writing, using pictures and diagrams.)

Andrew Brodie: Ten Minute Maths Assessments ages 7–8 © A&C Black 2009

Read the time to the nearest 5 minutes on an analogue clock

Name

Date

Write the correct time under each clock.
You may need to use some words from the word bank.

clock   quarter   half   past   to

5 past 3

I can read the time to the nearest 5 minutes.

Andrew Brodie: Ten Minute Maths Assessments ages 7–8 © A&C Black 2009

Extended assessment: Answer a question by collecting, organising and interpreting data

Building on previous learning

Before starting this unit check that the children can already:

- answer a question by collecting and recording data in lists and tables.
- represent data as block graphs or pictograms to show results.

Learning objectives

Objective 1: Answer a question by collecting, organising and interpreting data; use tally charts, frequency tables, pictograms and bar charts to represent results and illustrate observations; use ICT to create a simple bar chart.

Learning outcomes

The children will be able to:

- create an appropriate chart to show results in answer to the question: What is the most popular drink in your class?

Success criteria

The children have a **secure** level of attainment in relation to Objective 1 if the following questions can be answered with a 'yes'.

Can the children...
... decide which data to collect?
... collect the data systematically?
... organise the data they have collected?
... create an appropriate bar chart, pictogram or table to represent the data?
... answer the question about the most popular drink, and similar questions?

Administering the assessment

This is **not** a ten minute assessment! This activity provides the opportunity for a piece of extended work to assess the pupils against the framework in relation to handling data. Ensure that the children can read the instructions on the Assessment sheet. Help them to make appropriate decisions to be able to complete the activity. You may decide to use the grid template on page 96 to create sheets for the pupils to record their findings.

(This assessment will also provide evidence for assessing strand 1, Using and applying mathematics: Represent the information in a puzzle or problem using numbers, images or diagrams; Follow a line of enquiry by deciding what information is important; make and use lists, tables and graphs to organise and interpret the information; Describe and explain methods, choices and solutions to puzzles and problems, orally and in writing, using pictures and diagrams.)

Answer a question by collecting, organising and interpreting data

Name

Date

Favourite drinks

What is the most popular drink in your class?

Here are some different drinks: cola, milk, water, lemonade, orange juice, tea, coffee, hot chocolate.

Can you think of any other drinks?

When you have made your list of drinks, ask some people what their favourite drink is.

Find out how many people like each type of drink.

Draw a chart to show your results.

I can collect, organise and interpret data to answer a question.

Use Venn diagrams or Carroll diagrams to sort data and objects using more than one criterion

Building on previous learning

Before starting this unit check that the children can already:
- identify right angles in 2-D shapes.
- make and use lists and tables to organise and interpret information.
- describe, visualise, classify and draw 2-D shapes.

Learning objectives

Objective 1: Use Venn diagrams or Carroll diagrams to sort data and objects using more than one criterion.

Learning outcomes

The children will be able to:
- sort four shapes appropriately into Venn diagrams or Carroll diagrams using the criteria of 'has right angles' and 'has four sides'.

Success criteria

The children have a **secure** level of attainment in relation to Objective 1 if the following questions can be answered with a 'yes'.

Can the children…
… sort the shapes according to 'has right angles/has no right angles'?
… sort the shapes according to 'has four sides/does not have four sides'?
… sort the shapes according to 'has right angles/has no right angles' **and** 'has four sides/does not have four sides'?
… sort the shapes on to a Venn diagram?
… sort the shapes on to a Carroll diagram?

Administering the assessment

This activity is best suited to a one-to-one assessment. Prepare a large piece of paper with a Venn diagram with two overlapping rings, large enough for the square to fit in the overlap. Prepare a large piece of paper with a Carroll diagram of four regions. Discuss the shapes with the child. Ask her/him to sort the shapes according to the following criteria: 'has right angles/has no right angles'. Now ask her/him to sort them again: 'has four sides/does not have four sides'. Can s/he sort them on to the Venn diagram? Can s/he sort them on to the Carroll diagram?

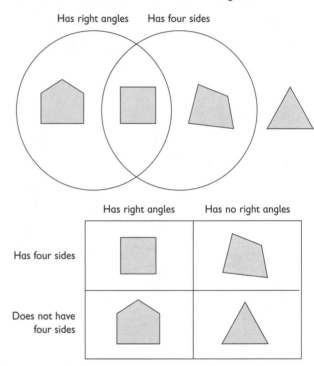

(This assessment will also provide evidence for assessing strand 1, Using and applying mathematics: Represent the information in a puzzle or problem using numbers, images or diagrams; use these to find a solution and present it in context; Follow a line of enquiry by deciding what information is important; make and use lists, tables and graphs to organise and interpret the information; Identify patterns and relationships involving numbers or shapes, and use these to solve problems; Describe and explain methods, choices and solutions to puzzles and problems, orally and in writing, using pictures and diagrams.)

Andrew Brodie: Ten Minute Maths Assessments ages 7–8 © A&C Black 2009

Use Venn diagrams or Carroll diagrams to sort data and objects

Name

Date

Cut out the shapes, and then listen to your teacher.

I can sort shapes using more than one criterion: having four sides and having right angles.

Supplementary sheet for use with Assessments 41 and 44

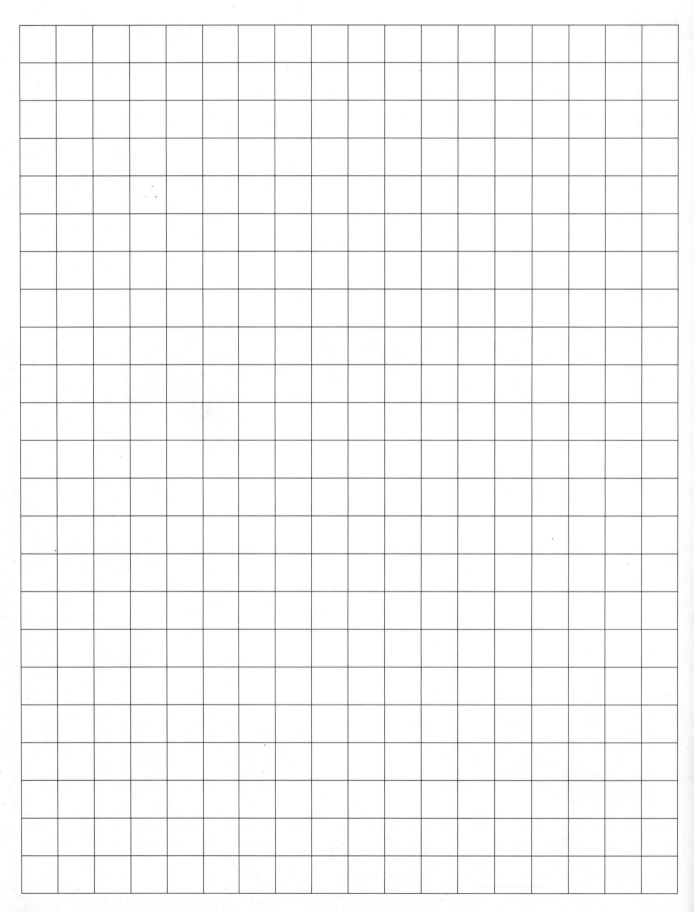